Rocks and

of the

Falkland Islands

by Phil Stone, Don Aldiss and Emma Edwards

Design: Deborah Rayner; Graphics: Chris Wardle; Editor: Joanna Thomas, all BGS. BGS Studio photography by Tom Bain and Fergus MacTaggart, field photography by the authors. Unless otherwise stated, the copyright of all images/illustrations is vested jointly in NERC and the Falkland Islands Government.

Additional photo credits:

Figure 11, Darwin fossil specimen; Figure 15, trilobite head and thorax; Figure 17 three views of trilobite head; Figure 59, fossil wood. ALL: ©The Natural History Museum, London.

Figure 29 (left), aerial view of stone runs, Department of Agriculture, Falkland Islands Government

Figure 61 (left), Pony's Pass Quarry, Alex Blake

Figure 65, agate pebbles, Brian Summers

Figure 74, gold particles courtesy of Derek Reeves, Falkland Minerals Limited.

Cover illustration: Smoko Rocks, East Falkland

Printed by Hawthornes, Nottingham, UK

Falkland Islands Government
Department of Mineral Resources

Bibliographic reference:
STONE P, ALDISS D T, and EDWARDS E J. Rocks and fossils of the Falkland Islands. British Geological Survey for Department of Mineral Resources, Falkland Islands Government, 2005.

ISBN 0 85272 494 2

In some of the illustrations the scale is obvious, in others the subject's size is mentioned in the caption or shown by a scale bar. Many of the illustrations include either a geological hammer or a Falkland Islands two-pence coin to give an impression of relative scale. In these cases, the hammer is about 30 cm long whilst the coin is 2.5 cm in diameter.

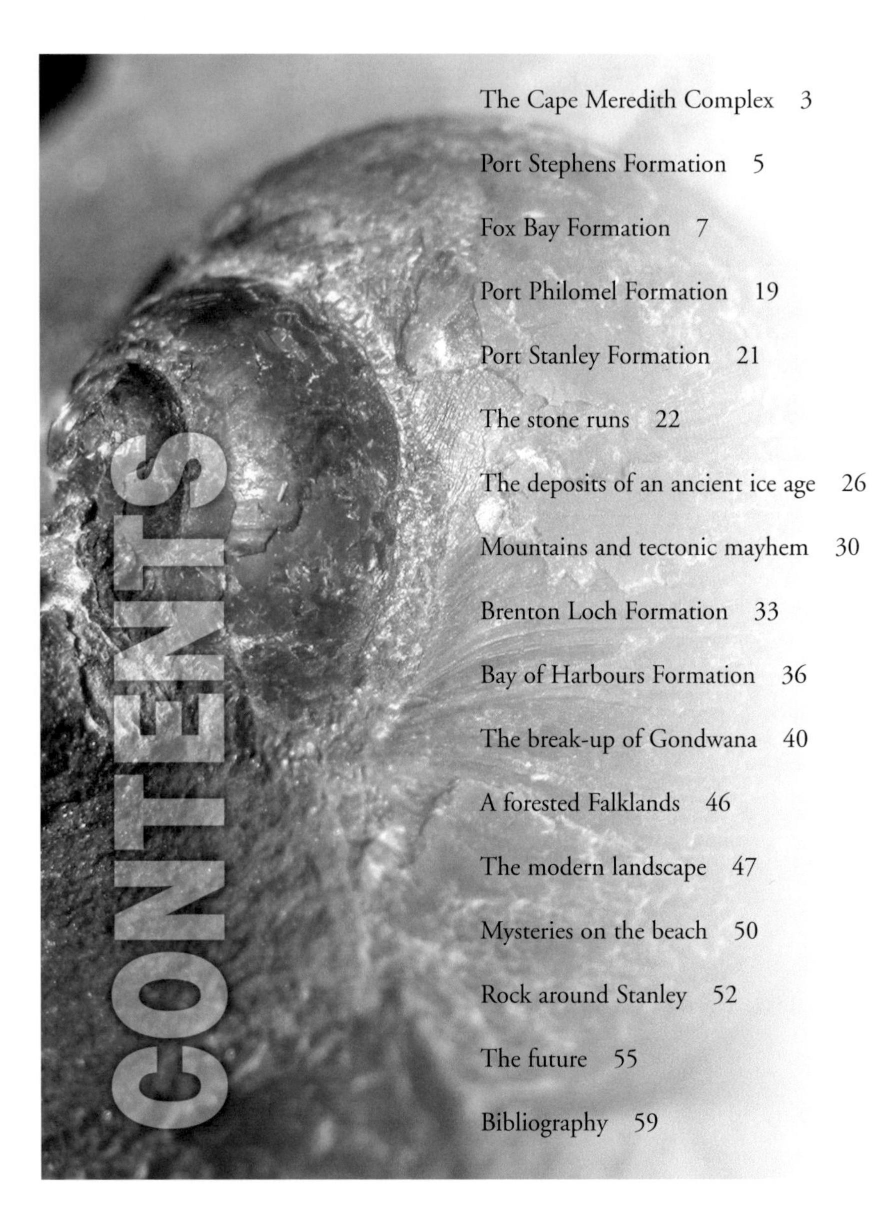

CONTENTS

Foreword

The Falkland Islands are justly renowned as a pristine environment of extraordinary and subtle beauty that is home to a wealth of fascinating wildlife. The very special character of the landscape is inherited from the underlying rocks and these, together with the fossils which they contain, reveal the secrets of another intriguing and very ancient world. The first steps towards understanding those secrets were taken by Charles Darwin during his voyage on *HMS Beagle*, and in the years since then many other scientists have made their own contributions. This accumulated background knowledge provided the foundation for the recent comprehensive study of Falklands geology completed by the British Geological Survey on behalf of the Falkland Islands Department of Mineral Resources. It was primarily undertaken to guide the continuing search for offshore oil and onshore minerals such as gold. However, the dramatic story told by the rocks is worthy of a much wider audience, and it is our hope that both islanders and visitors alike will enjoy this account of the origins of the Falkland Islands. It tells of former continents torn apart by cataclysmic tectonic forces and the fragments dispersed by newly expanding oceans, of life and death in ancient seas, of the eons of change that have made the Falklands what they are today. There is certainly a lot more to the islands than meets the eye, and much more still to be discovered about their remarkable geological history.

Phyllis Rendell
Director, Department of Mineral Resources, Stanley, Falkland Islands

ROCKS AND FOSSILS
of the Falkland Islands

Dean Street, Christ Church Cathedral and Stanley Harbour

It might seem bizarre, but the Falkland Islands are a fragment of Africa caught on the wrong side of the Atlantic Ocean.

This book tells the story of their origins and subsequent emigration to the New World. It was a tortuous journey during which north became south and the ocean floor was pushed up into mountains. It has taken us from an ancient ice age to another, more recent one, with fluctuating sea levels along the way. The evidence is preserved in the rocks and fossils now to be seen in the islands so, in a way, this account is their collective biography.

Hundreds of millions of years ago all of our present-day Southern Hemisphere continents were joined together in one huge landmass called *Gondwana* (Figure 1). But the crust of the Earth is not static. It is made up of huge plates, between 6 and 30 km thick, that move slowly across the face of the globe, floating on the dense, semi-molten rock beneath and driven by the convective heat flow deep inside the Earth. The crustal plates variously collide, move apart or slide past each other, producing irresistible tectonic forces that stretch some parts of the Earth's crust whilst squeezing other parts. Stretching causes thinning of the crust, subsidence and the formation of basins that fill with sediment; compression causes thickening of the crust as the rock layers fold and buckle to produce mountain belts. A stretched plate will eventually break, allowing new volcanic material to erupt and a new ocean to form between the

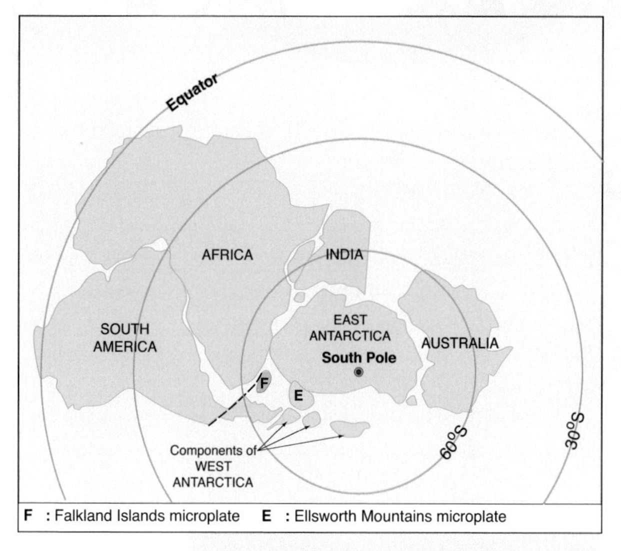

Figure 1 The ancient 'supercontinent' of Gondwana. The present-day southern hemisphere continents have been re-assembled as they were 300 million years ago and are shown in a south polar projection. The Falkland Islands slot in between South Africa and East Antarctica.

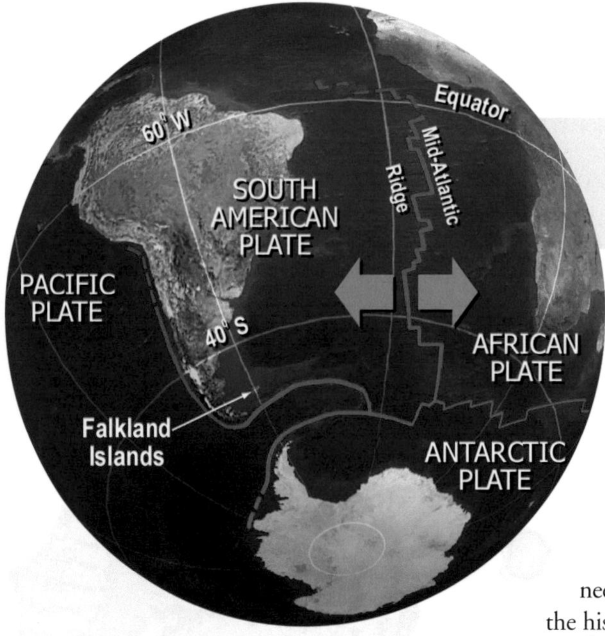

Figure 2 The Falkland Islands and the present-day geological plate configuration around the South Atlantic Ocean.

fragments of the old continent. Such was the fate of Gondwana.

As Gondwana broke up, starting about 200 million years ago, the South Atlantic Ocean opened between Africa, South America and Antarctica (Figure 2). Several small continental fragments were jostled and rotated during the upheaval. One of these, originating from a position adjacent to what is now the south-east coast of South Africa, was dragged around to the South American side. The main spreading zone of the embryonic Atlantic developed to the east of the displaced fragment and it was carried away westward along with South America, getting a few centimetres farther from its African roots every year. That wandering piece of Africa now underpins the Falkland Islands and their continental shelf.

The evidence for all this comes from the rocks and the fossils that they contain. But before we look at Falkland Islands geology in more detail, we need a general frame of reference for the history of the Earth itself. This is conventionally divided up into a series of named intervals (Frontispiece) to which an absolute timescale can be applied. How do we know the ages of rocks? Some originated as layers of sediment on the seabed or lake floors (so they are called *sedimentary* rocks) and contain the fossilised remains of animals or plants. These fossils can give a relative indication of age, with different fossil assemblages appearing in vertical succession (oldest at the bottom, youngest at the top) and each one having a lateral correlation with the same assemblage in other areas (Figure 3). Absolute, numerical age determinations are obtained by careful measurement of the proportions of the minor radioactive components in *igneous* rocks (that were once molten). These proportions are 'frozen-in' when the molten rock cools and solidifies, and thereafter the

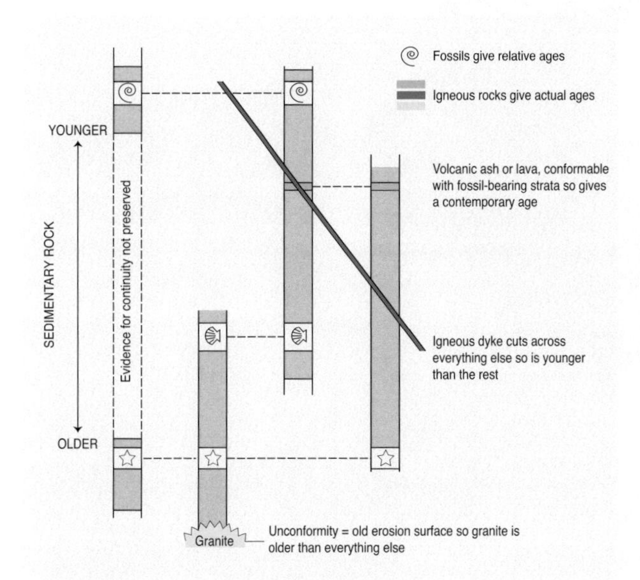

Figure 3 Sedimentary rock sequences in different places can be correlated by their fossils, and given an absolute age from their relationship with igneous rocks, which can be dated by careful analysis of their minor radioactive components.

radioactive elements decay steadily at a known rate. By integrating both kinds of evidence (Figure 3) we can build up an accurate timetable of when things happened.

So, back to the Falklands and another geological convention. At the local scale, distinctive sequences of rocks are named after geographical areas in which they are particularly well displayed. Hence, the Falklands sedimentary rock succession (Figure 4) carries a series of local names, but remember, these are just places where there are typical examples – the rocks concerned can usually be seen in lots of other parts of the islands as well. The final geological convention that we will follow in this look at Falklands rocks and fossils (with a few diversions along the way) is to always start at the bottom, with the oldest rocks, and work upwards towards the youngest rocks. This way we start closest to the beginning of everything.

And just to keep 'beginning' in perspective – the Earth itself (and the rest of the Solar System) formed about 4600 million years ago. Even that was quite recent in comparison to the approximately 13 400 million-year age of the Universe.

The Cape Meredith Complex

Precambrian, about 1000 million years old

The oldest rocks preserved in the Falkland Islands were formed 'only'

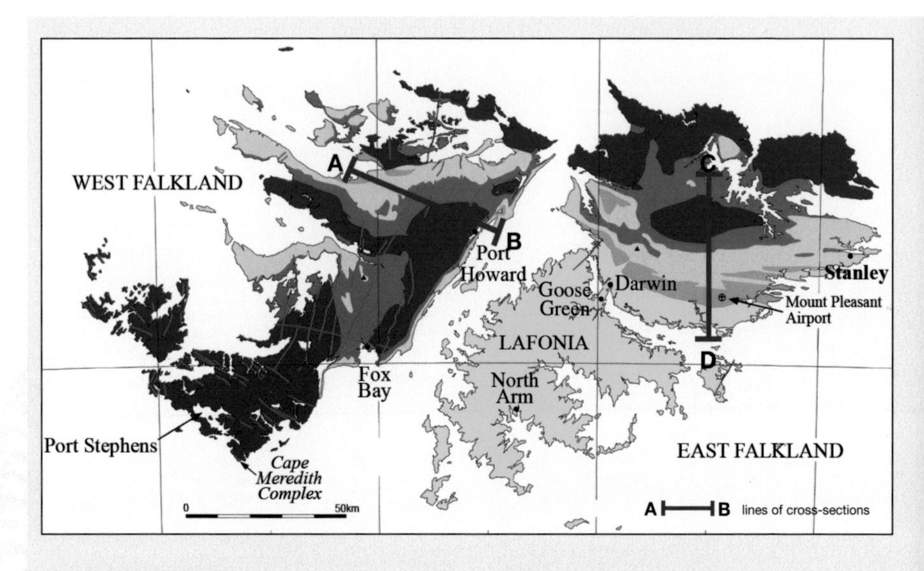
WEST FALKLAND
A
B
C
D
Port Howard
Goose Green
Darwin
Stanley
Mount Pleasant Airport
LAFONIA
Fox Bay
North Arm
Port Stephens
Cape Meredith Complex
EAST FALKLAND
0
50km
A B lines of cross-sections

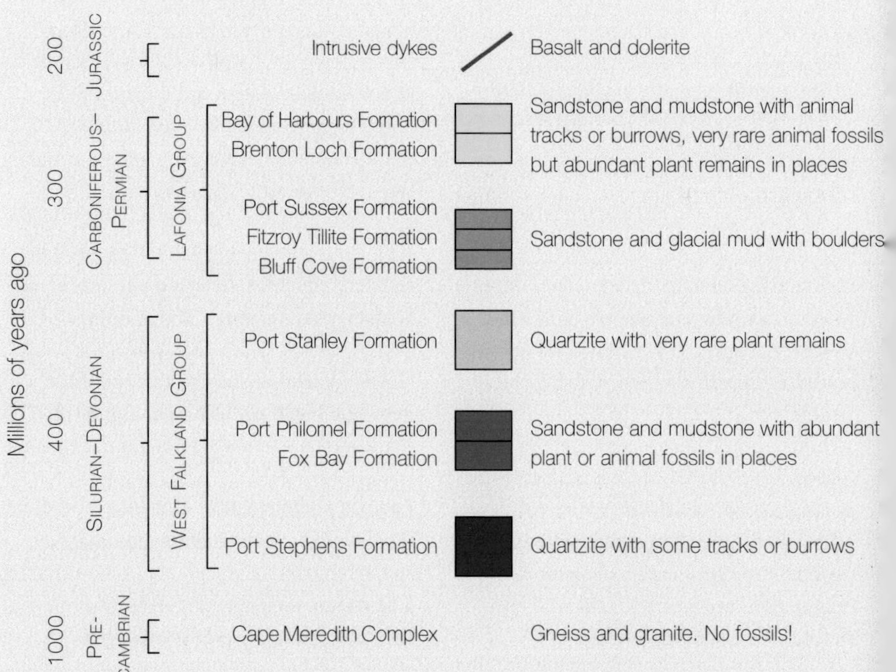
Millions of years ago
200
300
400
1000
Carboniferous–Permian
Jurassic
Silurian–Devonian
Pre-Cambrian
Lafonia Group
West Falkland Group
Intrusive dykes
Basalt and dolerite
Bay of Harbours Formation
Brenton Loch Formation
Sandstone and mudstone with animal tracks or burrows, very rare animal fossils but abundant plant remains in places
Port Sussex Formation
Fitzroy Tillite Formation
Bluff Cove Formation
Sandstone and glacial mud with boulders
Port Stanley Formation
Quartzite with very rare plant remains
Port Philomel Formation
Fox Bay Formation
Sandstone and mudstone with abundant plant or animal fossils in places
Port Stephens Formation
Quartzite with some tracks or burrows
Cape Meredith Complex
Gneiss and granite. No fossils!

Figure 4 A simplified geological map of the Falkland Islands showing the distribution of the main rock units. The two block diagrams give an idea of the disposition of the strata in three dimensions.

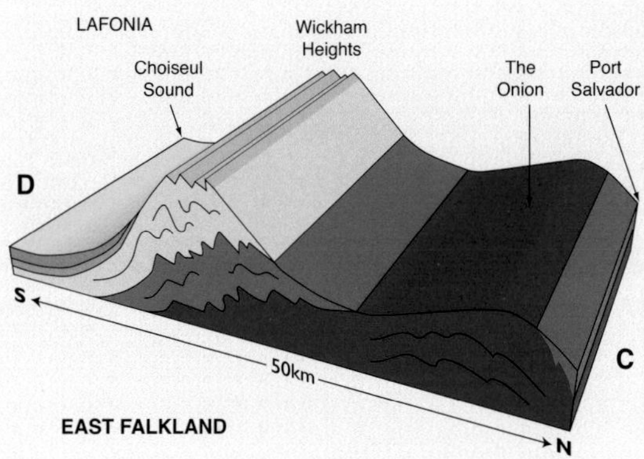

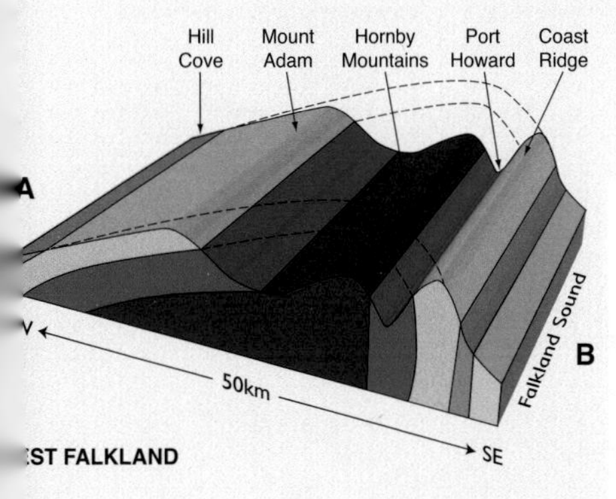

about 1000 million years ago. They are the granite (a familiar *igneous* rock type that crystallised slowly from molten magma deep in the Earth's crust) and gneiss (a *metamorphic* rock, i.e. one much changed by great heat and high pressure) that together form the Cape Meredith Complex. These hard, ancient rocks produce some spectacular coastal cliffs around Cape Meredith, the southernmost point of West Falkland (Figure 5), but are not seen at the surface anywhere else. Generally they remain deeply buried beneath a cover of the much younger sedimentary sequence (Figure 6).

Port Stephens Formation

Silurian, about 420 million years old and up to about 2500 m thick

We're not quite sure when the oldest of the sedimentary rock units, the Port Stephens Formation, was first laid down as layers of sand, but it was probably during the Silurian Period about 420 million years ago. This was a time when Gondwana was still intact, long before the Atlantic Ocean opened. The shoreline of Gondwana ran across what is now South Africa and was very close to the then adjacent Falklands, so that most of the older sedimentary rocks, the West Falkland Group (Figure 4), were deposited as sandy and muddy layers in a shallow-water coastal environment. They commonly preserve ripples and the cross-bedding formed by migrating sand bars. As time went on, the Gondwana shoreline crept across what would become the Falkland

Figure 5 The cliffs of Cape Meredith, West Falkland, formed by the granite and gneiss of the Cape Meredith Complex, part of the ancient crystalline heart of Gondwana.

Figure 6 Near Cape Meredith, West Falkland, the beds of sandstone at the base of the Port Stephens Formation rest unconformably on the granite and gneiss of the Cape Meredith Complex. More than 500 million years of geological history is missing across the contact.

Islands. Accordingly, the character of the sedimentary deposits gradually changed (upwards in the geological succession) to relatively coarse-grained, cross-bedded sandstones laid down by rivers.

The pale coloured, creamy brown Port Stephens Formation sandstones are hard and quartzitic for the most part, and contain small quartz pebbles in places. Locally, where they have a higher proportion of relatively unstable mineral grains, they are more prone to weathering and become quite crumbly, but they still form most of the high ground in the south of West Falkland and the north of East Falkland. Some of the higher crags have been eroded into fantastic shapes by the sand-blasting effect of Falklands gales over thousands of years (Figure 7). At Cape Meredith, the sandstones rest directly on the much older metamorphic rocks (Figure 6), which must have formed the sea floor on which the sand accumulated.

No actual animal remains have been found as fossils in the Port Stephens Formation rocks, but there are plenty of signs of life preserved; the burrows and tracks of presumably soft-bodied creatures

Figure 7 A wind-eroded pillar of Port Stephens Formation sandstone standing on the southern ridge of Mount Maria, West Falkland. The remarkable shape arises from the density of the sand grains carried by the wind being greatest close to the ground, so that is where the erosive sand-blasting is most effective.

are seen in many places. Quite common are traces of the vertical burrows once occupied by a type of tube-worm (Figure 8). In cross-section the beds of rock have a striated appearance whilst the surface of a bed, the original sea floor, is spotted with small round marks showing where the animals popped up to feed. This kind of 'trace fossil' is called *Skolithos*. Another kind, seen particularly well in the sandstones that overlie the Cape Meredith Complex, is a bit more mysterious (Figure 9). It was clearly made by something quite large working its way through the soft sediment, perhaps feeding, but we have no idea what the animal might have looked like, not even from modern analogues. The trace itself is called *Heimdallia*.

Fox Bay Formation

Devonian, about 400 million years old and up to about 1500 m thick

Above the Port Stephens Formation a different type of sandstone appears. It is mostly yellowish-brown and is interbedded with thin layers of black mudstone. This rather sudden change back to sea-floor deposits occurred because of a world-wide rise in sea level. Because these rocks are relatively soft and so are readily eroded, the Fox Bay Formation underlies most of the lower ground in the central parts of West Falkland and the northern part of East Falkland (Figure 10). The

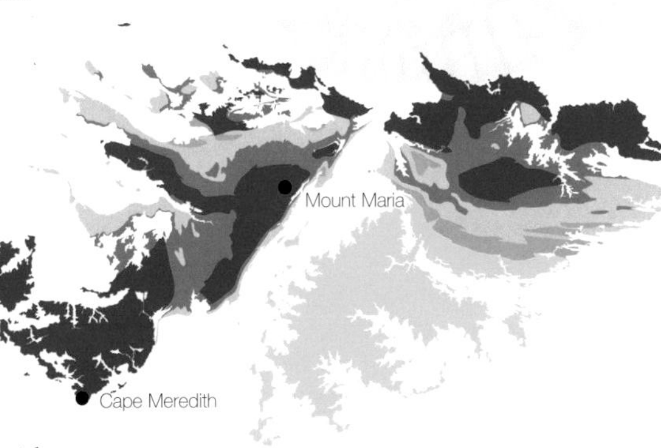

Figure 8 Aspects of the trace fossil *Skolithos* from sandstone of the Port Stephens Formation on Pebble Island, West Falkland. The striped rock surface (left) shows a cross-section through the vertical, tube-worm burrows, the spotted surface (centre) is the original sea floor and the spots show the position of the burrow entrances from which the animals emerged. The oblique view of the rounded boulder (right) shows how the two features go together.

most dramatic aspect of the Fox Bay Formation is that it contains fossils — lots of them. Charles Darwin first discovered them (Figure 11) at Port Louis in East Falkland, when he visited the Falklands on board HMS Beagle in 1833. Since then it has become clear that the best fossil specimens actually come from West Falkland; most of those from the East have been a little bit squashed during the subsequent folding of the sandstone layers — we'll come on to that later.

There is quite a range of fossil types present and their age is pretty well established. The original animals were all living in the shallow coastal waters of Gondwana during the early part of the Devonian Period, about 400 million years ago. They are all long extinct, but still have distant though very different relatives alive today. The same

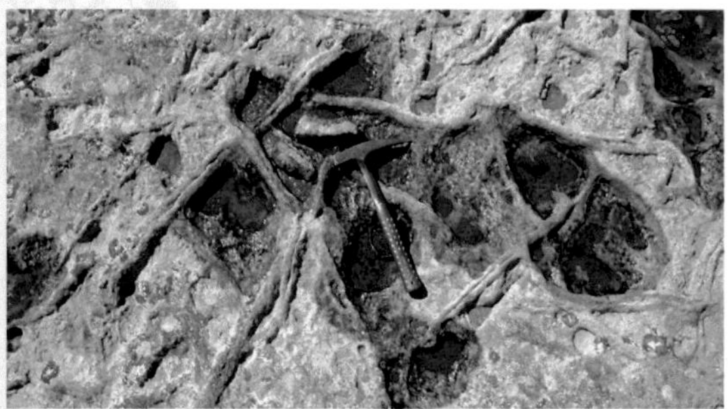

Figure 9 The trace fossil *Heimdallia*, from Port Stephens Formation sandstone near Cape Meredith, West Falkland, is the result of an unknown animal working its way through the soft sediment, perhaps feeding.

Figure 10 *Left* Looking south-west across the Chartres River towards Mount Philomel, West Falkland. All of the low lying foreground is underlain by the soft sandstones of the Fox Bay Formation; the distinct bench on the flanks of Mount Philomel is produced by near-horizontal strata of the Port Philomel Formation, whilst the hill is capped by hard quartzite of the Port Stanley Formation. *Below* Looking west across Port Salvador, East Falkland. The stone runs in the foreground and the distant Wickham Heights are all formed from hard, Port Stanley Formation quartzite; between these two areas, the low-lying ground around Port Salvador is underlain by the softer sandstones of the Fox Bay Formation.

assemblage of fossils as is found in the Falklands is also present in South Africa and parts of the Antarctic, and is also to be found in rocks of the same age scattered across South America, from Argentina to Bolivia. This distribution of fossils forms part of the evidence for the reconstruction of Gondwana shown in Figure 1.

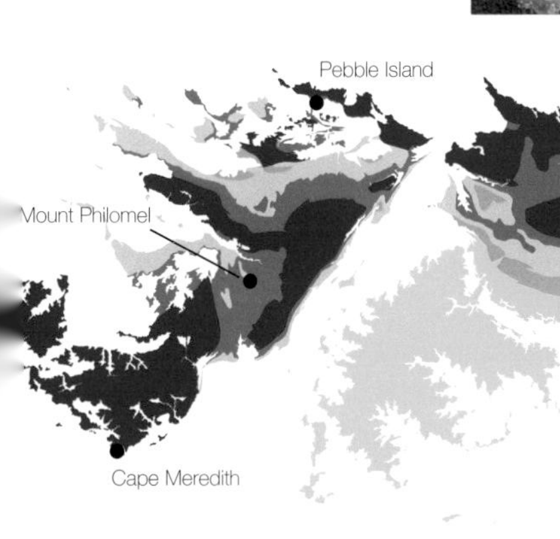

The commonest fossils are various kinds of brachiopod, a type of shellfish. There are shells from at least two different brachiopod species in Darwin's rock slab (Figure 11) — part of his collection now housed in The Natural History Museum, London — and a bigger

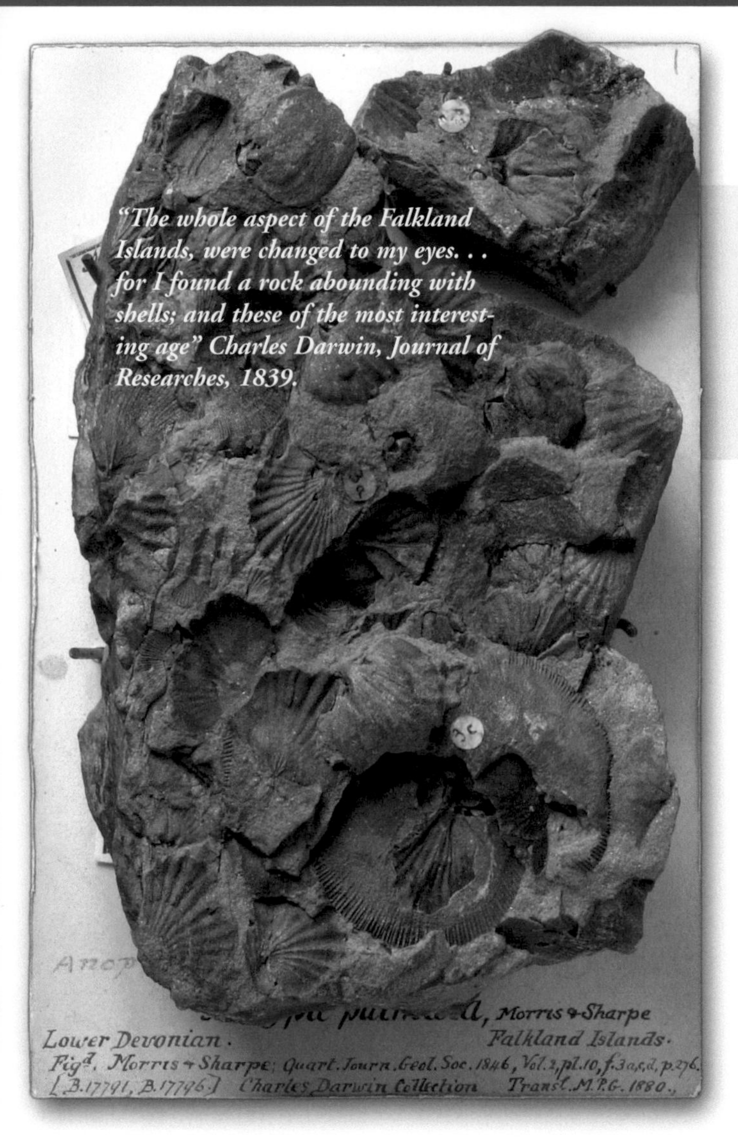

"The whole aspect of the Falkland Islands, were changed to my eyes. . . for I found a rock abounding with shells; and these of the most interesting age" Charles Darwin, Journal of Researches, 1839.

Figure 11 Fossil brachiopod shells from the Fox Bay Formation, collected in 1833 by Charles Darwin at Port Louis, East Falkland, during his voyage on HMS Beagle. © The Natural History Museum, London.

range can be seen on the other rock surfaces illustrated later.

But first it's useful to look at the way in which the fossil shells have been preserved. Where the original shells have been incorporated into a porous sandstone, the calcium carbonate of which they were made has been mostly dissolved away by water that has percolated through the rock over millions of years. So, what we have left are just the impressions of the original shells, now cast in sandstone. But to make matters more complicated, some of the impressions are of the inside of the shells and some are of the outside. In Figure 12 a specimen of the brachiopod *Schellwienella* has been split open so that the matching impressions of the inside and the outside of the original shell can be seen. What's more, a brachiopod's paired shells are not symmetrical mirror-images of each other, so they each leave different impressions. This means that each species of brachiopod can leave four different fossil impressions – and that's before we start to take account of the inevitable differences between individuals of the same species. Who said that identifying fossils was easy?

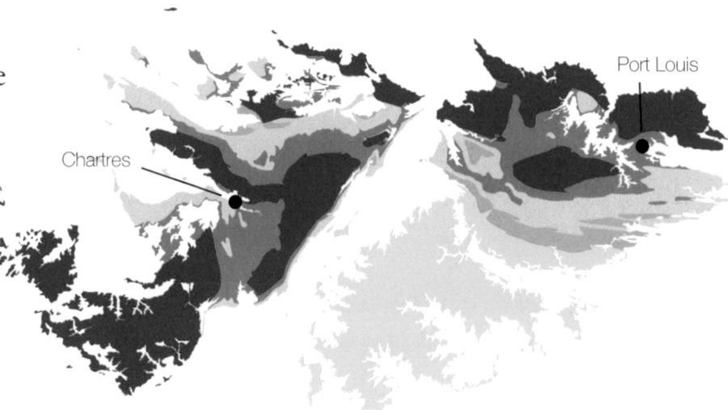

A selection of Falklands brachiopods is shown in Figure 13. The big, chunky 'winged' shells are called *Australospirifer*, whilst the small, more delicate ones are *Australocoelia*; the latter, together with fossils of *Schellwienella* are the types present in Darwin's specimen. In one of the specimens illustrated, the rounded, elongate shells of *Pleurothyrella* show something of the internal structure of the brachiopods. All of these shells were strong enough to have been widely preserved in three dimensions. In contrast, the shells of *Orbiculoidea* were probably quite delicate,

Figure 12 This piece of Fox Bay Formation sandstone has been split open to show the two sides of a fossil brachiopod shell: the mould of the inside is to the left, with the impression of the outside to the right. Scattered across the rock surfaces are small discs – the disaggregated remains of crinoids. This fossil specimen was collected near Chartres, West Falkland, and is now in the collection of the Sedgwick Museum, Cambridge.

Fox Bay
Schellwienella
sulivani
3 cm
Australospirifer
hawkinsii
3 cm
Port Louis
Harbour
1 cm
Pleurothyrella
falklandica
Dan's Shanty C
Port Salvador

Figure 13 Some of the more common brachiopod fossils from the Fox Bay Formation. The larger rock slabs carry several different species and some trilobite fragments (circled).

asymmetric cones and have almost invariably been flattened into discs.

These collections of shells are the remains of sea-floor shell banks; the animals died and their shells became disarticulated as the currents washed them into heaps, perhaps during storms. There they were buried in the drifting sand and disappeared from sight for 400 million years. Brachiopods lived (and a few varieties still do) by drawing seawater into their shells and filtering out food particles. Their different shapes probably arose through the evolution of slightly different feeding strategies.

In amongst the brachiopods there may be other types of fossils, and in the specimens illustrated crinoids and parts of trilobites can also be seen. Whilst these do occur in the sandstone, the crinoids quite widely, both they and the trilobites are more common and better preserved in the finer grained, mudstone. There, the fossils are commonly encased in a calcium carbonate concretion that developed as the soft sediment hardened into rock. This has preserved the original shells and protected the fossil from deformation during the subsequent folding of the rock layers.

Figure 14 Fossilised lengths of crinoid stalk in Fox Bay Formation mudstone, Pebble Island, West Falkland. More commonly, when the crinoid died, the stalks broke up into the dozens of constituent discs.

Crinoids are related to sea urchins and starfish but are often called 'sea-lilies' because they looked rather like plants. They had a long, flexible stem, made up of lots of small hard discs and anchored to the sea floor, on top of which was a cup carrying five feathery arms which collected any food particles that drifted past. These waving fronds were quite fragile and are rarely preserved as fossils. In contrast, the hard, tough stalks are common as fossils, sometimes with lengths of several centimetres intact (Figure 14) but more

Figure 15 Fossilised remains of the homalonotid trilobite *Burmeisteria herscheli*. All three of these pieces were collected from the Fox Bay Formation at Pebble Island, West Falkland, but the top two of the illustrations – the head shield (cephalon) and segmented thorax, but not the tail piece (pygidium) – are © The Natural History Museum, London. The accompanying sketch shows how they fitted together in an idealised trilobite of calmoniid type.

On the whole, Falklands trilobites preferred mud. Their fossils are much more common in the fine-grained mudstone than in the coarser sandstone. Trilobites had to moult in order to grow, and so most of their fossilised remains are only fragments of the discarded shell. This shell, really an external skeleton, consisted of rigid shields at the head and tail, joined by a number of articulated segments (Figure 15) that allowed the trilobite to roll up into a ball for protection. For extra protection, some trilobites were

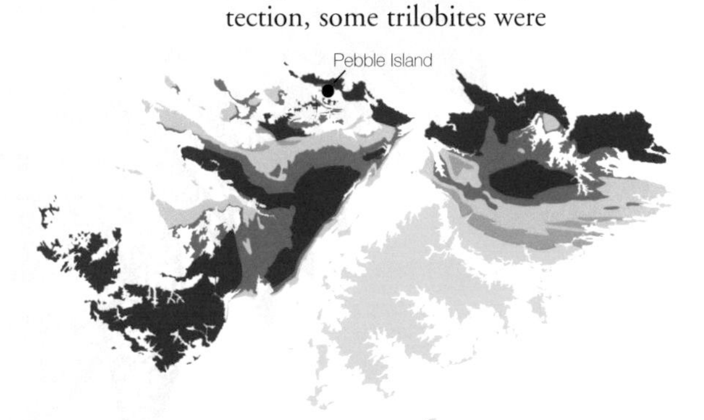

often broken-up into the constituent discs (Figure 12). These little round 'ossicles' are widely scattered through the Fox Bay Formation rocks.

Figure 16 The back of this partly rolled-up calmoniid trilobite stands out from the rock surface and clearly shows the three longitudinal body lobes that are characteristic of trilobites. The fossil specimen was collected near Chartres, West Falkland, and is now in the collection of the Sedgwick Museum, Cambridge.

covered in spines, and the sockets for such spines can be seen in the picture.

Two main types of trilobite are found in the Falklands – homalonotids and calmoniids, with the former the more common. The calmoniids, like the one illustrated, (Figure 16) have the three characteristic longitudinal divisions of the body well defined (that's why they're called tri-lobe-ites), but these three divisions are much less obvious in the homalonotids, as in the picture (Figure 15) of the

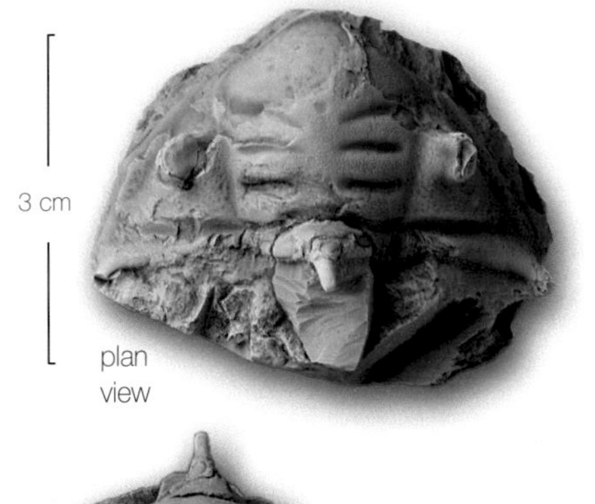

front view

4 cm

side view

Figure 17 The head shield of the calmoniid trilobite *Bainella nilesi*: plan, front and side views. © The Natural History Museum London. The specimen has been expertly prepared in The Natural History Museum, by Dr Adrian Rushton. It was collected in a carbonate concretion from Fox Bay Formation mudstone at Pebble Island, West Falkland, and illustrates the remarkable detail to be seen in fossils from that locality. Notable features preserved in this example are the occipital spine and the individual lenses of the compound eye.

Figure 18 A fossil snail, *Naticopsis*, from a carbonate concretion in Fox Bay Formation mudstone, Pebble Island, West Falkland. Preservation is sufficiently good to show the individual growth lines in the shell. The snail is about 2.5 cm across.

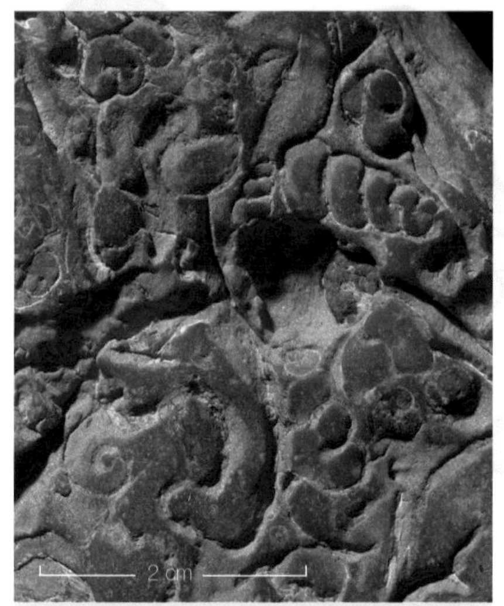

Figure 19 Small, spiral shells of the snail *Loxonema* in a carbonate concretion from Fox Bay Formation mudstone, Pebble Island, West Falkland.

trilobite called *Burmeisteria*. Some trilobites, like *Burmeisteria*, probably crawled around on the sea bed, scavenging for food, but others might have been free-swimming or predatory. Whatever their lifestyle, good eyesight was a distinct asset. Different views of the head shield of the calmoniid trilobite *Bainella* (Figure 17) clearly show the well-developed eye stalk, with the side view in particular picking out the individual lenses of the animal's compound eye. *Bainella* also had a very impressive spike on the top of its head.

The muddier parts of the sea floor were also home to a multitude of snails and a range of small bivalve shell-fish. Most common as fossils are the broad, coiled shells of the snail *Naticopsis* (Figure 18), some with the growth lines clearly

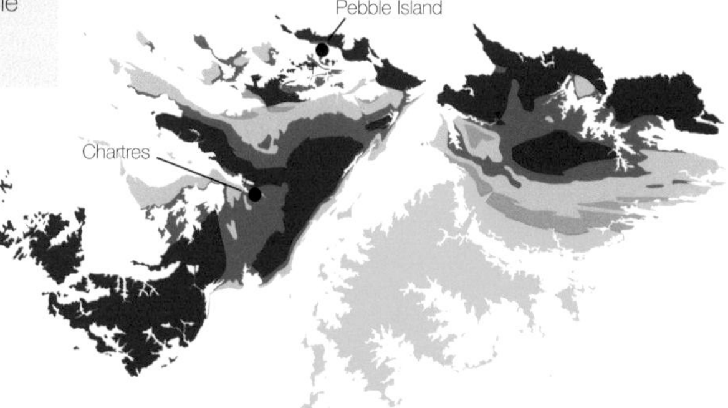

Figure 20 Another fossil snail from a carbonate concretion in Fox Bay Formation mudstone, Pebble Island, West Falkland. This shell was overgrown by bryozoa after the snail died but before it was buried in sediment. The snail is about 2.5 cm across.

preserved. Less common are the generally smaller and more tightly coiled, pointed shells of *Loxonema* (Figure 19). Sometimes the abandoned shells of dead snails were colonised by other organisms as in the example shown (Figure 20) where the snail shell has a coating of bryozoa.

The bivalves lived rather like the brachiopods but they and their multitude of modern descendents (mussels, scallops, oysters etc.) have a very different internal anatomy from the brachiopods. The Falklands bivalves from the Fox Bay Formation tend to be small, smooth and inconspicuous (Figure 21). Those shown in the illustration are accompanied by enigmatic little conical shells called *tentaculitids* (Figure 22). Large numbers of fossil tentaculitids are sometimes found aligned, as if they had been draped across the sea bed by a prevailing current and it is possible that they floated around in planktonic fashion. Some species of tentaculitids certainly lived like that, but the variety found in

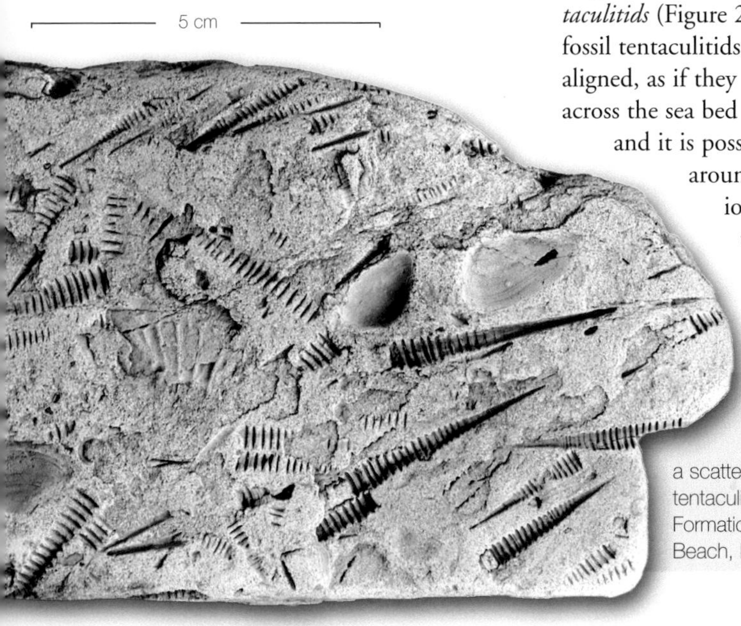

5 cm

Figure 21 The internal moulds of several small bivalves and a scattering of screw-shaped tentaculitid fossils from Fox Bay Formation sandstone at Elephant Beach, Foul Bay, East Falkland.

Figure 22 Screw-shaped tentaculitid shells scattered across sandstone of the Fox Bay Formation from Dan's Shanty Creek, Port Salvador, East Falkland.

the Falklands more probably enjoyed a sea-floor existence.

Most of the fossils described so far are those of animals that lived on the sea floor and were buried there in its sediment cover when they died. But there were also animals swimming in the sea above, and sometimes their remains have also become fossilised after their dead bodies fell to the bottom. *Orthocones* might well have been top of the Fox Bay pecking order. They had long, pointed shells containing a number of segmented chambers (Figure 23); the largest one at the open end of the shell occupied by the animal and the others used to control buoyancy. They probably had a lifestyle similar to that of modern squid (a very distant relation), seizing their prey with flexible tentacles.

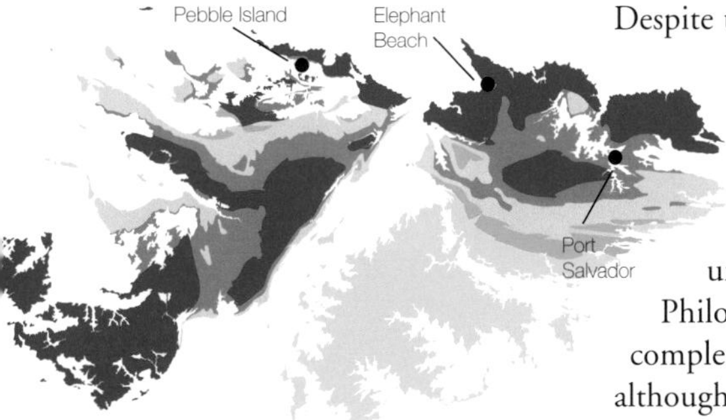

Pebble Island
Elephant Beach
Port Salvador

Port Philomel Formation

Devonian, about 390 million years old and up to about 350 m thick

Despite the abundance of animal remains preserved in the sand and mud of the Fox Bay Formation, the good times didn't last. Overlying the Fox Bay strata is another unit of sandstones, the Port Philomel Formation, which is almost completely devoid of animal fossils, although microscopic traces of scales and teeth suggest that fish were around.

Figure 23 A cut section through a carbonate concretion from Fox Bay Formation mudstone at Pebble Island, West Falkland. Two tapering, chambered orthocone shells and the rounded shells of several snails have been intersected.

Instead of animal fossils, the Port Philomel Formation contains lots of plant material. Maybe the Falklands part of the Gondwana coast had become more estuarine, with a large river washing down driftwood but also introducing fresher water that didn't suit the marine population. The fossil wood fragments are mostly preserved only as carbonaceous smears, but sometimes the pattern of leaf scars on twigs and branches can still be seen (Figure 24); each of the oval or diamond-shaped marks on the surface of the fossil wood shows where a leaf was attached.

Figure 24 Fossilised wood from the Port Philomel Formation, a lycopsid stem from Port North, West Falkland.

Figure 25 Tabular cross-bedding seen in quartzite of the Port Stanley Formation on the shores of Cape Pembroke, East Falkland. The cross-bedding formed as currents washed the sea floor sand into submarine dunes and bars, the oblique lamination arising as sand grains cascaded down the steep front of the advancing sand bodies. In one example (above) we can deduce a current flowing broadly from right to left (that's towards the north in present-day terms) but things are a bit more confusing where the strata have been pushed over to become near vertical (above, right). More on that later, for the moment just remember that the sea floor was originally horizontal!

Port Stanley Formation

Devonian, about 370 million years old and up to about 1100 m thick

Above the Port Philomel Formation is the youngest unit of the West Falkland Group, the hard, white quartzites and intervening softer sandstones and mudstones of the Port Stanley Formation that were deposited about 370 million years ago. Quartzite is a type of sandstone, but one made up largely of quartz grains that have fused together rather than being cemented by a finer grained matrix. A few fragments of fossil wood have been found in the lowest quartzite beds of the formation, and some of the mudstones contain microscopic plant spores, but the Port Stanley Formation does not seem to contain any animal fossils, and even

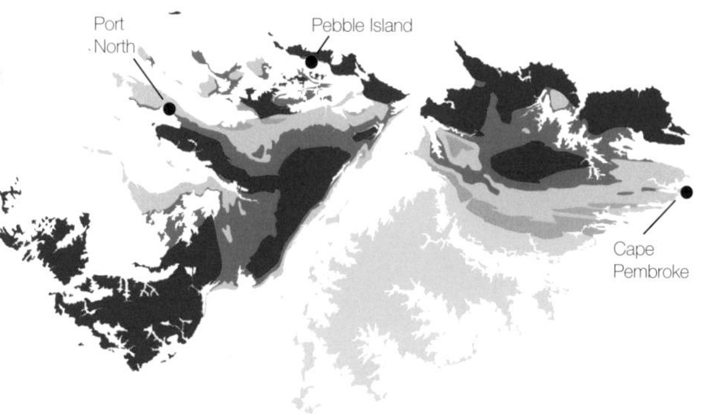

their burrowing traces are exceedingly rare.

The quartzite probably started off on the sea floor in huge submarine dunes and sheets of clean white sand, and the cross-bedding that formed as these dunes and sand-sheets advanced across the more muddy substrate is commonly picked-out by modern weathering of the rocks (Figure 25). This effect is particularly pronounced along the coast but can also be seen along the length of the Wickham Heights, because the hard, white quartzite forms the mountainous spine that runs from east to west across East Falkland (Figure 26). These mountains include Mount Usborne, at 705 m the highest point on the islands. The quartzite also makes up the highest ground in West Falkland, around Mount Adam in the northern part of that island. Other spectacular Falklands features closely associated with the Port Stanley Formation quartzite are the stone runs. It's worth a digression from our evolving geological story to take a look at them.

Figure 26 The rugged landscape created by the hard quartzites of the Port Stanley Formation, seen here looking west from Mount William towards the Wickham Heights, East Falkland.

The stone runs

When Charles Darwin explored the Falklands in 1833 he noted in his journal that *'In many parts of the islands the bottoms of the valleys are covered in an extraordinary manner by myriads of great loose angular fragments of the quartz rock,*

forming "streams of stones" … They are not thrown together into irregular piles, but are spread out into level sheets or great streams.' Darwin's description is hard to beat. The vast spreads of quartzite boulders (Figure 27) are impressive enough, but equally remarkable are the series of stripes that break up the margins of the larger boulder spreads and occur independently in other places. The patterns are pretty astonishing at ground level (Figure 28) but can be absolutely breathtaking when seen from the air (Figure 29). From a casual glance it might look as if the stripes had been produced as linear zones of vegetation grew across the boulder spreads, but this is not the case. Rather, plants have colonised strips of stony soil that separate the lines of boulders.

Figure 27 An extensive stone run (or *periglacial blockfield*) made up entirely of large blocks of quartzite derived from the Port Stanley Formation. The view looks southwards from the southern slope of Mount Challenger, East Falkland.

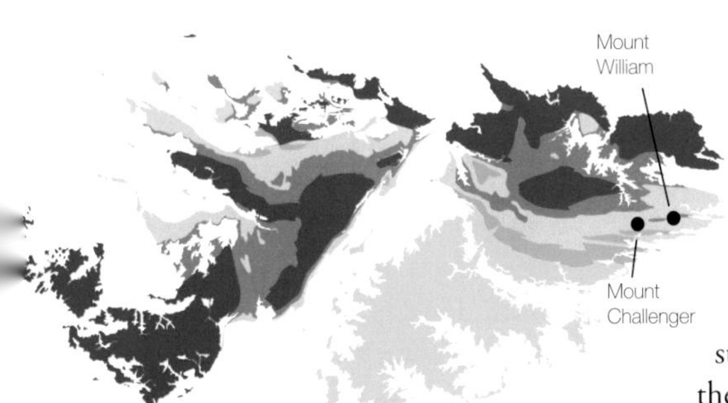

Figure 28 Stone run stripes on the southern slopes of Mount Challenger, East Falkland. The colour contrast is enhanced by white lichen colonising the grey quartzite boulders, dark green and brown ferns and diddle dee growing along the well-drained margins of the vegetated stripes, and paler white grass occupying the centres of the vegetated stripes.

So how on Earth were the stone runs formed? The answer lies back in the last Ice Age (a series of cold interludes that culminated about 15 000 years ago) when the Falklands were a frigid, tundra-like wilderness. The islands supported only a few small glaciers on the highest ground but the surface covering of loose rock debris, sand and mud was mostly locked into permafrost. Only the top metre or so thawed and refroze with the seasons, or maybe on a daily basis. One effect of all of the freezing and thawing was to shatter any exposed quartzite into great loose boulders, whilst the softer rocks were broken down completely to form stony, sandy clay. As this process went on, year after year, through thousands of freeze-thaw cycles, the boulders gradually crept downhill, carried along with all the other semi-frozen debris. As they did so, something very strange happened. Each time the moisture in the soil froze, it grew into masses of ice coating the larger boulders, so they were gradually separated from the stony mud in between, and pushed together in discrete zones, aligned downhill on even the gentlest of slopes. Meltwater produced when the ice thawed was channelled into the open

spaces between the boulders and washed away the remaining sand and mud. Eventually, after tens of thousands of years, the stone runs were produced.

Why the link with the Port Stanley Formation quartzite? Good question, because the stone runs are not unique. They might be the biggest and most spectacular example of 'periglacial blockfields and blockstreams' in the world, but smaller versions of the same phenomenon are found wherever there has been a relatively recent ice age, and similar features are still forming today in areas underlain by permafrost. The answer is probably that the quartzite breaks up naturally into such large boulders, whereas most rocks similarly affected by millennia of freezing end up as sand and gravel. From the big boulders we get big stripes and it's very hard for

Figure 29 The spectacular patterns produced by the stone runs are best seen from the air. These examples lie on the southern slopes of Mount Challenger, East Falkland. The more distant view (left) is about 2 km across, the closer view (below) spans several hundred metres.

vegetation to get a grip on them. It's quite possible that much smaller stripes were formed all over the Falklands, from all sorts of different rocks, but these have long ago vanished beneath the peat, white grass and diddle dee.

The deposits of an ancient ice age

Carboniferous, about 300 million years old

The signs of a very much earlier ice age, one that occurred about 300 million years ago, are preserved in the rock record on the Falkland Islands. There is a break in the sequence at the top of the Port Stanley Quartzite (which is also the top of the West Falkland Group – see Figure 4), which might represent as much as 100 million years. We don't know the details of what happened during that interval, but it came to an end as the Earth slipped into one of its periodic spells of intense cold. The sandstone and mudstone of the *Bluff Cove Formation* (which is up to 250 m thick) are the lowest strata assigned to the Lafonia Group but show little sign of what was to come. Indeed, the presence in the mudstone of rare plant spores and pollen grains show that vegetation was present on nearby land areas. But, as the ice sheets advanced, conditions changed and distinctive types of glacially transported sediment were deposited. Since the Falklands region of Gondwana was still down in the higher latitudes of the southern hemisphere (Figure 1) it was soon covered by ice sheets and the glacial debris that they carried.

The first signs of the advancing ice are the isolated, large boulders that appear in the sandstone and mudstone above the Bluff Cove Formation; these arrived on floating icebergs and dropped to the sea floor as the ice melted (Figure 30). Soon the whole area was covered by ice,

Figure 30 Laminated sandstone and mudstone deposited on the sea floor but containing isolated pebbles that dropped out of melting icebergs that floated far above; the pebbles are derived from a wide range of rock types. These features are well seen in the Fitzroy Tillite Formation at Quark Pond, West Falkland.

Figure 31 Across much of East Falkland, as shown at Frying Pan Quarry near Mount Pleasant Airport, the Fitzroy Tillite Formation comprises a massive rock type in which pebbles and boulders, mostly of quartzite or granite, are enclosed in a matrix of sandy mudstone.

from which was deposited a blanket of sand, mud and boulders of all shapes and sizes – the largest boulder so far found in the Falklands was more than 7 m across! Rock formed from this heterogeneous mixture is known as tillite (recent glacial deposits formed in the same way are called till) and in the Falklands became the *Fitzroy Tillite Formation* (which is up to 850 m thick). Most of the Fitzroy Tillite is a massive rock in which no bedding can be seen. The basal layers of sandstone containing exotic, ice-rafted boulders testify to the advance of the ice sheets, whilst rare layers of mudstone and sandstone show that there were brief periods when the climate was less severe and the glaciers temporarily retreated. At Hill Cove in West Falkland, pockets of sand occur within the tillite and were probably deposited by meltwater streams. There is a curious difference between the Fitzroy Tillite found in East and West Falkland. In the east, the tillite is a dark grey, massive muddy rock containing an array of pebbles and cobbles of various rock types, mostly quartzites and granites (Figure 31). In the west, the matrix is more sandy, and the enclosed clasts are more abundant, range up to larger sizes, and are formed from a greater range of rock types (Figure 32). We think that the difference is caused by a change in the original glacial environment from east to west. In the east, the ice sheet was floating on the sea and its debris accumulated on the sea floor in a background of marine mud. In the west, the ice sheets were still onshore and the

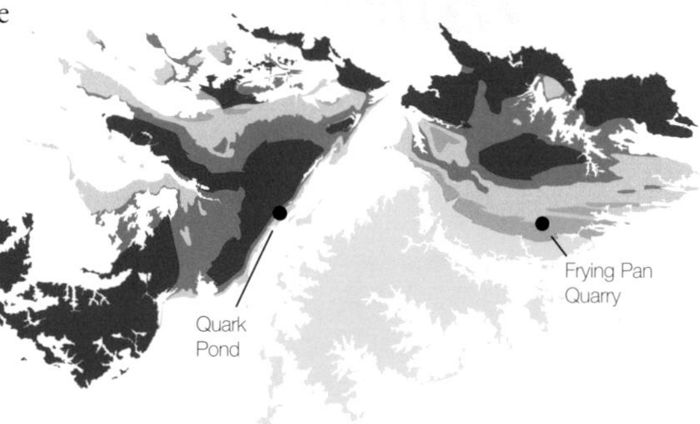

Figure 32 On the north coast of West Falkland, near Hill Cove, the Fitzroy Tillite Formation forms cliffs in which pebbles and boulders of a wide range of rock types are enclosed in a sandy matrix. The boulders are eroded from the cliffs and accumulate on the beach beneath as an extraordinary collection of rocks entirely alien to the Falkland Islands. The general view of the cliff (right) shows a large block of limestone adjacent to the hammer; the close-up view (above) shows a block of laminated red quartzite and blocks of different types of granite.

tillite accumulated as terrestrial glacial moraines.

Despite the differences between east and west, all of the tillite pebbles and boulders were probably derived originally from the same area, the part of Gondwana that was in the vicinity of the South Pole 300 million years ago. That was what is now East Antarctica (Figure 1), and it is back in much the same position today. Amidst all the various rock types in the tillite that are totally alien to the Falklands — the granites, the metamorphic rocks, the lavas, the limestone — it is the rare limestone pebbles that provide the most crucial evidence of the link with Antarctica. They contain fossils, and pretty uncommon ones at that. Many of the limestone blocks in the

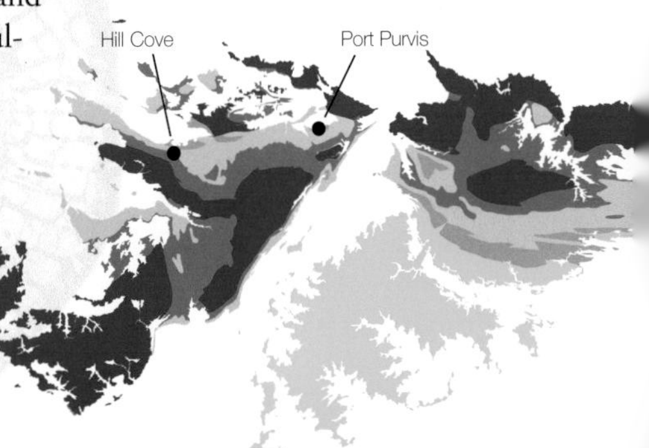

Fitzroy Tillite contain the remains of archaeocyaths, types of primitive sponges that lived only during the early part of the Cambrian Period (Frontispiece), becoming extinct about 500 million years ago. That's 100 million years before the animals now fossilised in the Fox Bay Formation were around. The only place in the Falklands region of Gondwana where rocks of that age, and with archaeocyath fossils, are found today is in the Transantarctic Mountains, part of East Antarctica. Quite a few different species of archaeocyath are present in the far-travelled, Fitzroy Tillite limestone blocks, but they all share a common basic body plan; two inverted cones, one inside the other, are joined by various arrangements of septa. Sometimes the details of the fossils can be plainly seen on the

Figure 33 Two views of archaeocyath fossils in a limestone block from the Fitzroy Tillite Formation at Port Purvis, West Falkland. Cross-sections (below) and a longitudinal section (below right).

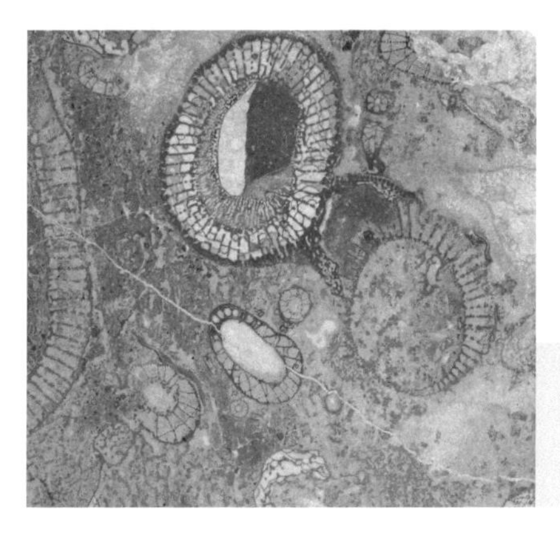

Figure 34 The fine detail of the archaeocyath fossils is shown in this cut section of a limestone block recovered from the Fitzroy Tillite Formation near Hill Cove, West Falkland.

Figure 35 Upended beds of Port Stanley Formation quartzite form the rugged cliffs and ridges of the Wickham Heights, East Falkland. The northern side of Vantan Arroyo clearly shows the steeply inclined strata.

weathered surfaces of the limestone blocks (Figure 33), but the best views are seen when the fossils are cut into very thin, transparent slices and examined through a microscope (Figure 34).

Eventually the ice sheets covering Gondwana retreated. Exotic boulders are not seen in the mud and sand that became the rocks of the *Port Sussex Formation* (which is up to 400 m thick). First came black and carbonaceous mud, a lifeless accumulation beneath water with very little dissolved oxygen, and then more sandy sediment was introduced as the environment livened up again. Other things were changing too, and in the upper part of this formation there is evidence for an upsurge in volcanic activity — thin beds of clay that were once layers of volcanic ash, and grains of volcanic rock in the sandstones. The latter can only be detected when the rock is cut (like the archaeocyaths) into thin sections, studied through a microscope and subjected to mineralogical analysis. The volcanic activity was a sign that massive forces were beginning to stir deep within the Earth's crust. The history of the Falklands was about to get violent.

Mountains and tectonic mayhem

Permian, from about 280 million years ago

Starting about 280 million years ago were major changes at the Falklands' margin of Gondwana. Things had been fairly quiet for hundreds of millions of years, allowing the rock succession to build up undisturbed. Now the Earth's plate tectonic engine went into reverse and the layers of rock were squeezed, folded and thrust over each other and piled up into a mountain range along the margin of Gondwana. In the process the once-flat

strata were upended and folded, so that now, in the Wickham Heights for example, many of the Stanley Quartzite beds are steeply inclined (Figure 35). In the same area of East Falkland the many folds to be seen amongst the contorted beds of rock attest to the power of the forces involved, and the shape of the folds establishes the direction in which those forces operated. The consistent asymmetry of the folds in the Wickham Heights (Figure 36) shows that the rocks were pushed from north to south. At the same time, in response to the increase in pressure and temperature, new platy

Figure 36 Folded beds of Port Stanley Formation quartzite in East Falkland. At the western end of Wall Mountain (left and below) the folds show the asymmetry that allows deduction of the direction in which the tectonic forces responsible were operating. Some folds are large enough to form entire hillsides, as in the example (below left) from the Wickham Heights.

Figure 37 A strong cleavage cutting across thin beds of sandstone and mudstone from the Bluff Cove Formation near Fitzroy, East Falkland. In the more distant view from Shell Point (left), the beds undulate gently from top left to bottom right but are cut by cleavage planes inclined from top right to bottom left. In the close-up view from Memorial Cove (below) the attitudes of the bedding and cleavage remain the same, but the cleavage is so strong that the original bedding is contorted and almost obliterated in places.

minerals grew in the rocks perpendicular to the forces that were squeezing them. These new minerals produced a new plane of splitting, or cleavage, in the rocks, which is particularly well developed in some of the thinly bedded sandstones and mudstones of the Bluff Cove and Port Sussex formations (Figure 37).

In general, the strata of East Falkland were much more intensely affected by the folding than were those of West Falkland. Folds found in the west are much broader and more gentle than in the east, and the cleavage seen in many of the mudstones in the east fades out westwards. But where folds are well developed, not only the rocks were deformed. In the east, the fossils contained in the Fox Bay Formation were also squeezed and, in places, twisted slightly out of shape; in contrast, those from the west maintain their original shape. Check back to the pictures of the Fox Bay Formation brachiopod fossils (Figure 13) and compare the shells from different localities.

As the huge mountain belt developed along the margin of Gondwana it increased the thickness of the Earth's crust in that region, and hence its weight. So, the newly mountainous region of the crust sagged into the Earth's hot and more plastic interior and a huge surface depression spread out around the mountains. It eventually became a vast inland lake into which poured sediment eroded from the mountains and destined to become the youngest series of rock layers now seen in the Falklands. Curiously, whilst the smashed and crumpled rocks of the growing mountains were depressing the Earth's crust, the resulting lake flooded southwards across glacial tillite deposits that were in front of the mountain belt and so were still undisturbed. This means that in the south of the Falklands, in Lafonia, the Lafonia Group continues upwards from the glacial beds of the Fitzroy Tillite Formation, up into the lacustrine Brenton Loch and Bay of Islands formations.

Since the Lafonia Group strata south of the Darwin isthmus are relatively undeformed, the beds of sandstone and mudstone still lie fairly flat. This feature, coupled with the uniform softness of the rocks, has produced the topographically-subdued, rolling landscape of Lafonia. The characteristic long, low ridges trending east–west are produced by the gentle scarp and dip-slope effect of the slightly sloping rock beds.

Brenton Loch Formation

Permian, about 280 million years old and up to about 3000 m thick

The older of the two formations that underlie Lafonia comprises a range of sandstones and mudstones with abundant signs of animal life, though the fossilised remains of the lake-dwelling animals are very rare and have been found at only one locality — so far. Near Rory's Creek, on the south side of Choiseul Sound, a few small and very ordinary-looking bivalve shells have been

Figure 38 A fossilised pair of bivalve shells from the very top of the Brenton Loch Formation. Fossils like this have so far been found at only one locality across the outcrop of the entire Lafonia Group – at Rory's Creek on the southern shore of Choiseul Sound, East Falkland.

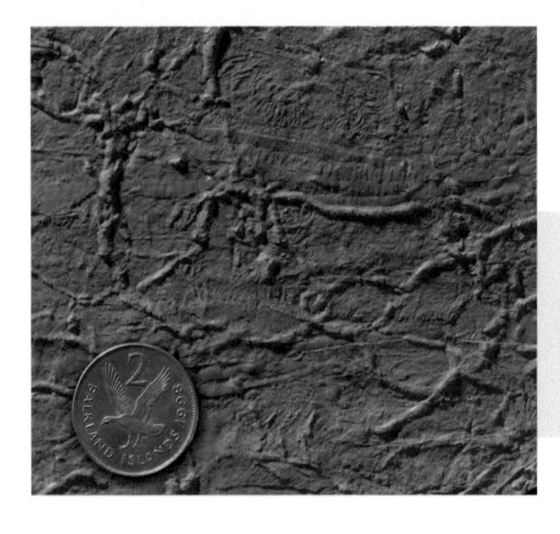

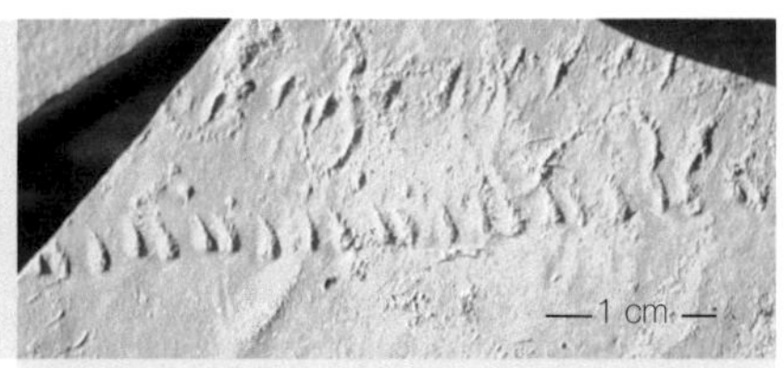

Figure 39 The irregular burrows and trails produced by worms as they worked their way through the sediment that has now become the Brenton Loch Formation. Trace fossils like those shown (left), from Canada Runde, near Darwin, East Falkland, are fairly widespread in this formation. A different style of trace fossil — a track left behind by a multi-legged arthropod (and known as *Umfolozia* after a famous occurrence in South Africa) — is seen in the example (above) from Swan Inlet, East Falkland.

recovered (Figure 38). There are also a few traces of plant material, but most of the 'fossils' are the crawling and burrowing traces of soft-bodied animals whose remains have not been preserved; they are trace fossils (Figure 39). The more irregular of the crawling traces might have been made by worm-like creatures, we don't know for sure. Other traces appear to be rows of tiny footprints left behind as a small arthropod scurried across the bed of the lake. A different type of trace fossil consists of parallel, sinuous lines left behind by fish (Figure 40). As they swam a meandering course close to the lake's bed, perhaps feeding on the worms and arthropods, the fishes' fins trailed in the mud to produce an undulating pattern of parallel grooves.

Figure 40 These sets of sinuous, parallel grooves, preserved in finely laminated sandstone of the Brenton Loch Formation at Camilla Creek, East Falkland, were made by fish. As they swam close to the bed of the vast lake in which the Lafonia Group strata were deposited, their fins trailed across the soft sediment. The interpretation is taken from Trewin, N. 2000. *Palaeontology*, Volume 43, 979–997.

Sedimentary conditions in the vast lake were fairly quiet for most of the time, with sediment drifting in through nearby river deltas. The mud and sand built up steadily, sometimes in finely laminated layers (Figure 41) that might be the result of seasonal fluctuations in river flow. Every now and again though a great mass of turbulent, saturated sediment would pour into the basin, perhaps as a result of flooding or a huge landslide set off by an earthquake (remember that the mountains were still growing, up to the north). The sudden influx of sediment, carried along in its own 'turbidity current' was powerful enough to scour and erode the lake bed so that pieces of the muddy floor were ripped up and incorporated into the sediment mass. As the current flowed further out into the lake it slowed down and could no longer support its sediment load. This then fell to the bottom of the lake, first the biggest pieces such as the flakes of ripped-up mud (Figure 42) then progressively smaller grains of sand, silt and mud. The result is a

Figure 41 Finely laminated sandstone and mudstone of the Brenton Loch Formation at Camilla Creek, East Falkland. The laminae might indicate seasonal variation in sediment input to the Lafonia Group lake.

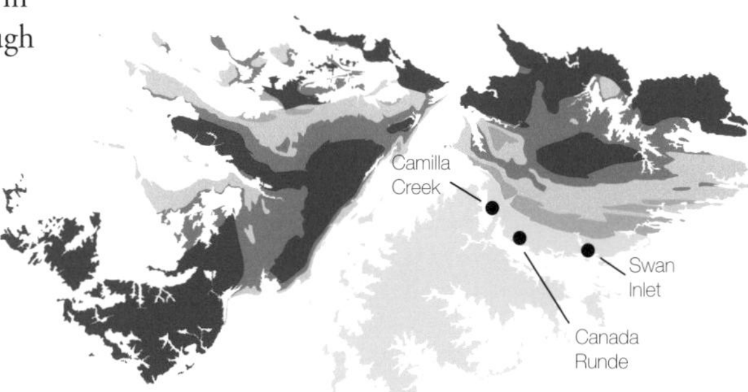

Figure 42 A mass of mud flakes at the base of a Brenton Loch Formation sandstone bed, Canada Runde, near Darwin, East Falkland. The mud flakes were eroded from the lake's bed as the sand was carried in as a great turbulent mass of water and sediment.

'graded bed' that starts off quite coarse at its base but then becomes finer grained upwards.

A curious and striking feature of some Brenton Loch Formation sandstones is the presence of rounded structures caused by the preferential erosion of concretions, balls of rock with a slightly unusual chemical composition that was acquired as the original sediment was transformed to stone. These concretions are usually nucleated on scraps of carbon-rich mudstone, which influenced developments in a more-or-less spherical zone of the surrounding sediment (remember the fossil-bearing concretions in the Fox Bay Formation at Pebble Island). The rock formed in this 'sphere of influence' may be softer or harder than is normal for the Brenton Loch Formation and so is either eroded away to leave a circular hollow (Figure 43) or left behind as a rounded protrusion.

Figure 43 The oval hollows left behind by the weathering of carbonate concretions in the Brenton Loch Formation, Sea Lion Island.

Bay of Harbours Formation

Permian, about 270 million years old and up to about 3000 m thick

As time went by, around about 270 million years ago, the deltas advanced across the lake floor so that in a vertical succession the laminated strata of the Brenton Loch Formation are succeeded upwards

Figure 44 Feathery cross-bedding picked-out by thin mud laminae in Bay of Harbours Formation sandstone at Salinas Beach, on the Brenton Loch side of Goose Green, East Falkland.

by the more variable sequence of mainly sandstone that makes up the Bay of Harbours Formation. The sandstones probably accumulated in a network of interconnecting delta channels. Feathery cross-bedding (Figure 44) shows how mud occasionally draped over the sand ripples that were being washed down the channels, and quite extensive spreads of ripples are preserved on some surfaces (Figure 45). The latter suggest that the lake was quite shallow in places and some parts of the delta top might have periodically emerged from the water. Rare, thin layers of clay that occur within the sandstone succession started off as accumulations of volcanic ash, showing that the volcanoes were still active not too far away.

There is an abundance of plant fossils in some parts of the Bay of Harbours Formation, the remains of driftwood carried down by the rivers and stranded amidst the delta sand bars. Once buried, some of the pieces of driftwood were petrified with every detail of their cellular structure replaced by silica. The fine detail of the original wood, such as the annual growth rings, can still be clearly seen (Figure 46). More commonly, the plants are preserved as impressions of their stems or leaves. Striated and jointed stem impressions (Figure 47) were probably produced by pieces of giant horsetail-like plants. Leaf impressions (Figure 48) might be related to the pieces of petrified wood and were derived from trees called *Glossopteris*. These trees were one of the common features of

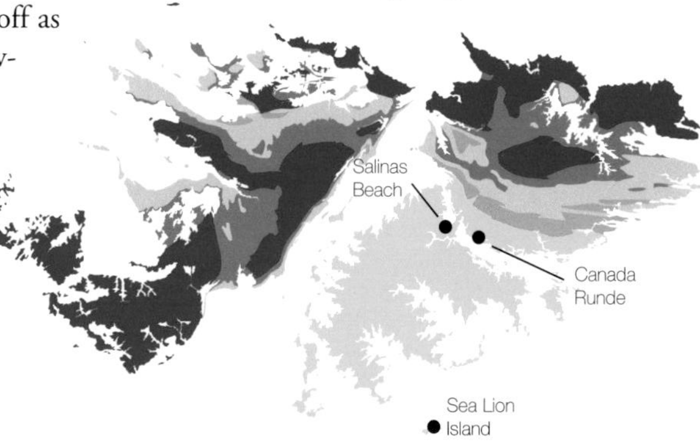

Figure 45 Lake bed ripples preserved in sandstone of the Bay of Harbours Formation at Newhaven, Lafonia, East Falkland.

Gondwana 250 million years ago, and their remains are found in rocks of that age right across Africa (Figure 49), India, Antarctica, Australia and South America. The *Glossopteris* trees and the horsetails grew in an environment that was probably cool and marshy.

Figure 46 Petrified wood fragments from the Bay of Harbours Formation on Bleaker Island, East Falkland. The annual growth lines are clearly preserved and suggest that fragments of quite large trees floated out as driftwood across the Lafonia Group lake.

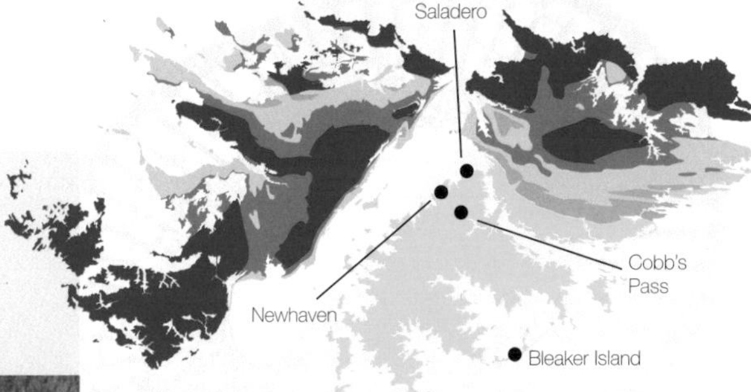

Figure 47 The striated stem of a horsetail-like plant preserved as an impression in Bay of Harbours Formation mudstone, Cobb's Pass, Lafonia, East Falkland.

weathering, initiated by the percolation of water through cracks and joints in the rock. As the water soaks into the rock adjacent to the cracks, so the unstable minerals that the rock contains become hydrated and softened. The areas affected are then more readily weathered and elaborate, spheroidal structures appear.

Strange rounded patterns in some Bay of Harbours Formation sandstones (Figure 50) are the effect of differential

Figure 48 Impressions of *Glossopteris* leaves from Bay of Harbours Formation mudstones near Saladero (below) and Cobb's Pass (right), Lafonia, East Falkland.

Figure 49 Glossopteris trees flourished across much of Gondwana and their fossilised leaves are widely preserved in strata of equivalent age to the Lafonia Group. The distribution of this ancient terrestrial flora was one of the first lines of evidence cited (by Alfred Wegener in 1912) in support of continental drift and the previous juxtaposition of the Southern Hemisphere continents. The example shown comes from South Africa; the similarity to the Falklands specimens is striking.

The break-up of Gondwana

Jurassic, from about 200 million years ago

The beginning of the end for Gondwana started about 200 million years ago with a massive upwelling of molten rock from deep inside the Earth. As irresistible tectonic forces tore the ancient continent apart, sheets of magma were forced up into the vertical cracks that cut across the pre-existing rocks. As the magma cooled, it crystallised into basalt and dolerite; hard, dark-coloured rocks containing iron-rich minerals such as pyroxene and olivine. The solidified sheets are now seen as

Figure 50 Spheroidal weathering of a thick sandstone bed, Bay of Harbours Formation, Newhaven, Lafonia, East Falkland.

igneous 'dykes' up to several hundred metres across that, in some cases, run for tens of kilometres across the Falklands. The dykes are most common and extensive in West Falkland (Figure 51) where they have baked and hardened their host rocks so that they now form long, straight topographical features (Figure 52). There are fewer dykes on East Falkland, but a large one cuts prominently across Lively Island, its course marked by a ridge topped with weathered and lichen-covered boulders (Figure 53); it might even link up, closer to Stanley, with a dyke in Pony's Pass Quarry (Figure 54).

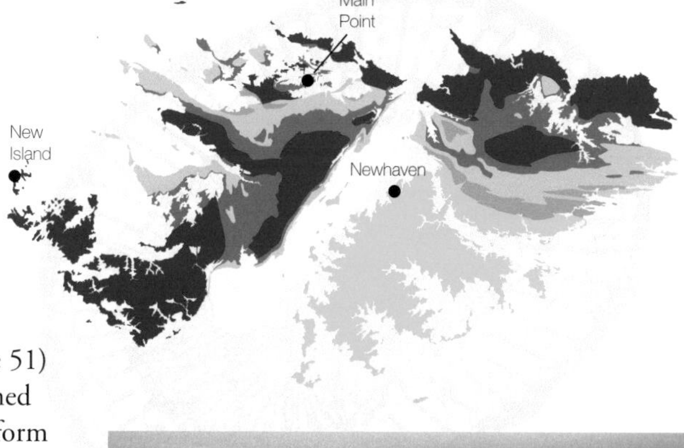

Figure 52 The linear topographic effect of a dyke cutting across the northern part of West Falkland: from Crates Point (bottom left), across the Main Point headland and Golding Island, to Pebble Island (top right).

Although the dolerite and basalt forming the dykes are very hard rock types, they tend not to be chemically stable in the presence of water. This means that some of the dykes have suffered the same kind

Figure 51 A dolerite dyke cutting sandstone of the Port Stephens Formation on New Island, West Falkland.

Figure 53 A large dolerite dyke cutting across the Lafonia Group strata of Lively Island, East Falkland, its course marked by a ridge capped with boulders that have been preferentially colonised by white lichen.

of spheroidal weathering that was described earlier for the Lafonia Group sandstones. The Lively Island dyke provides good examples of this phenomenon, with another clear instance seen at Port Sussex (Figure 55). In some cases, the chemically unstable dykes have proved more susceptible to weathering than the surrounding host rocks, particularly where these have been hardened by their contact with the hot magma. Then, the dyke lies within a linear hollow rather than forming a ridge.

As more dykes were intruded into fragmenting Gondwana the pieces of the original continent moved further apart, ocean spreading zones began to become established, and our present-day geography began to evolve. The dykes cutting across the Falklands confirm one unexpected part of that process — the small continental block carrying the islands was rotated through 180º, so that Jurassic north became present-day south. There is some evidence for this in the comparison of Falklands' geology with that of South Africa. Although the rocks and fossils are very similar, the structure is back-to-front. In South Africa, the Cape Fold Belt has been

Figure 54 A black dolerite dyke cutting grey quartzite of the Port Stanley Formation and exposed in Pony's Pass Quarry, near Stanley.

Figure 55 Spheroidal weathering of dolerite dykes produces a characteristic accumulation of rounded boulders, as seen in East Falkland at Port Sussex (left) and on the south coast of Lively Island (above).

pushed northwards with the Karoo Basin ahead of it; in the Falklands, the equivalent fold belt forms the Wickham Heights and has been pushed towards the Lafonia sequence (equivalent to that of the Karoo Basin), which is now to the south of it. The Falklands dykes provide remarkable confirmation of this apparent rotation. As the molten magma solidified and iron-rich minerals crystallised, a trace of the contemporary magnetic field was preserved. Modern technology allows this faint trace to be deciphered and it shows that the Falklands dykes appear to record a magnetic field running in the opposite direction to the one derived from dykes of the same generation in South Africa.

The decay of the minor radioactive components of the dykes allows them to be dated, so that we know they were

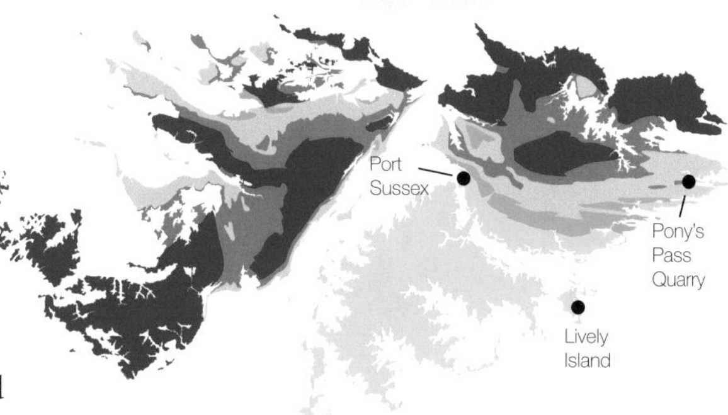

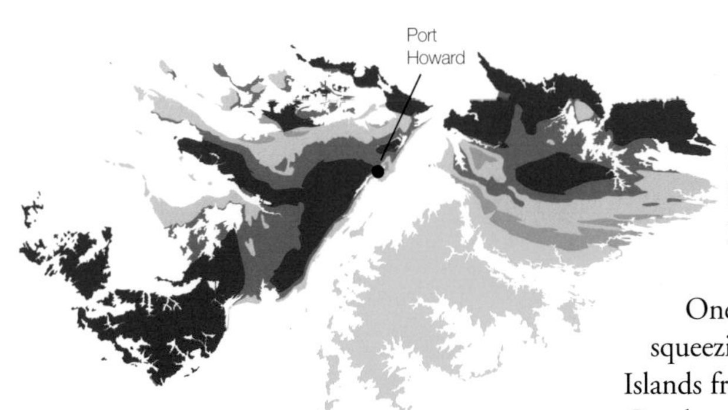

broken away and spun off to become the Ellsworth Mountains in Antarctica.

intruded about 190 million years ago. The record of spreading in the sedimentary basins of the Atlantic Ocean goes back about 160 million years. In between, during an early phase in the break-up of Gondwana, the small continental fragment that would eventually underpin the Falkland Islands broke away from Africa and was twisted around (Figure 56) into proximity with South America. Its near neighbour in Gondwana was similarly

One can imagine the jostling and squeezing suffered by the Falkland Islands fragment of continental crust as Gondwana succumbed to the massive tectonic forces. Huge fractures and folds developed — and these now produce some remarkable features of the modern Falklands landscape, such as the eastern coast of West Falkland. This is unlike any other part of the Islands. In contrast to the winding,

Figure 56 The break-up of Gondwana and rotation of the Falkland Islands continental block shown diagrammatically.

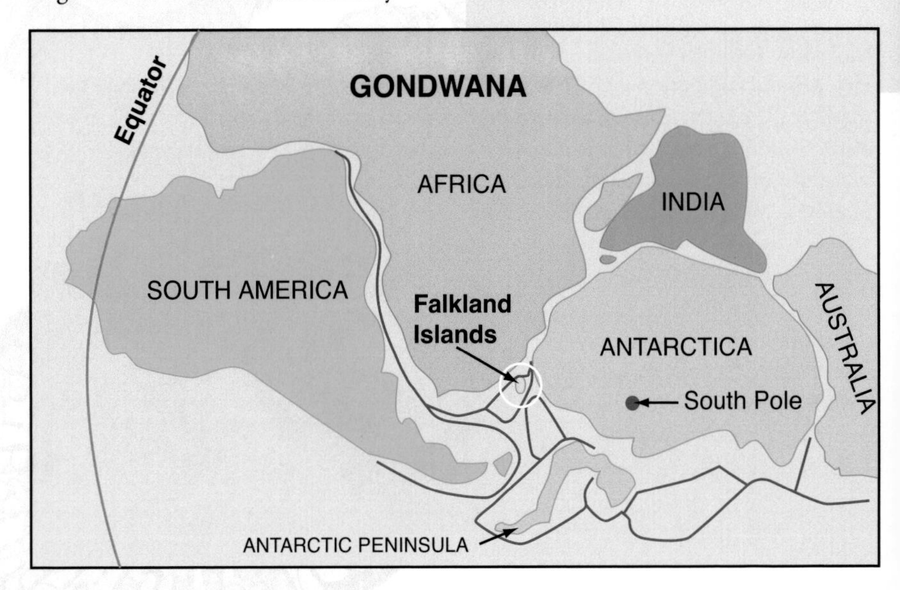

intricate embayments found elsewhere, it is remarkably linear and is bounded by a rampart-like ridge overlooking Falkland Sound. In places this rampart has been breached, as at the entrance to Port Howard (Figure 57), and the sea has flooded in over the lower-lying ground inland. The Coast Ridge is formed by hard quartzite of the Port Stanley Formation, the originally flat beds now upended to become vertical. The softer and more readily eroded sandstone of the Fox Bay and Port Philomel formations, their beds also now vertical, underlies the inlets like Port Howard. In this zone of vertical strata one can walk across the whole sedimentary sequence (Figure 4), from the Silurian to the Permian, in the space of a few kilometres.

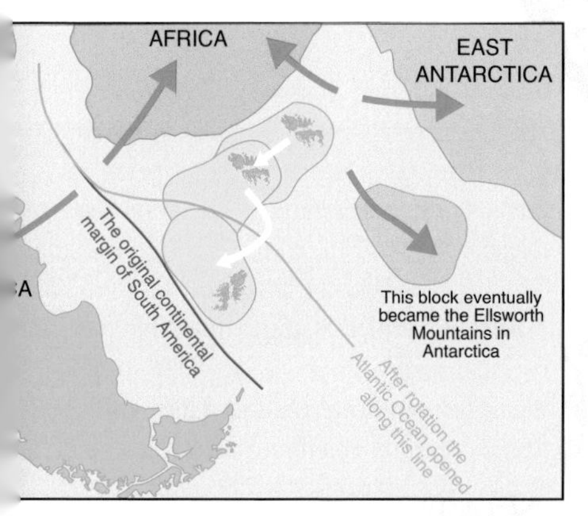

The strata were turned vertically on end during some particularly crushing tectonic episode, when a huge fracture developed beside what is now Falkland

Figure 57 The Coast Ridge and Port Howard, West Falkland. In the aerial view, the Coast Ridge snakes from bottom left to top right along the east coast of West Falkland, beyond are Falkland Sound and the distant coast of East Falkland. The upright beds of Port Stanley Formation quartzite that form the Coast Ridge have been breached at Port Howard, allowing the sea to flood in over the softer, more readily eroded sandstones of the Port Philomel and Fox Bay formations. Compare this view with the 3D sketch adjacent to the geological map on pages 4 and 5 (Figure 4). The ground level view looks east across Port Howard to the Coast Ridge and its serrated crest of quartzite crags.

Sound. The piece of continental crust carrying West Falkland was squeezed upwards against that carrying East Falkland and the whole great overlying pile of sedimentary rocks was left draped over the fracture lines, like a pile of tablecloths caught by a folding table. There are more subtle indications that an equally dramatic uplift occurred within East Falkland, but there the eastern part was raised relative to the west of the island with the differential movement taken up across myriad faults running parallel to Falkland Sound. One important topographical effect of this was the down-faulting of a block of strata that now forms the Darwin isthmus.

A forested Falklands

Neogene, about 7 million years ago

There is no evidence left to tell us what happened to the Falklands as its continental foundation drifted westwards, carried ever further from its African roots by the expanding Atlantic Ocean. But we are afforded a tantalising glimpse of the Falklands a mere 7 million years ago by a unique deposit on West Point Island, way out to the west of West Falkland (Figure 58). There, preserved beneath a covering of stony clay and peat, are the remains of trees. When first discovered in about 1900 the trees were thought to be of fairly recent origin; hence the description on the contemporary label of the specimen shown (Figure 59), from the collection of The Natural History Museum, London. A more informed assessment of the regional environment subsequently made this interpretation highly unlikely and so the occurrence was then widely dismissed as a chance accumulation of ancient driftwood incorporated into the relatively recent peat beds. However, as more detailed studies were made, it was realised that the trees had actually been growing close to where they were found and were covered by materials emplaced during the last Ice Age. Long ago, before the Ice Age, the Falklands had once supported a forest! Our best estimate of its age is about 7 million years.

The types of trees present are those that now grow in South America only north

Figure 58 West Point Island, West Falkland. The 'buried forest' is preserved at beach level around the shore of the harbour to the left of the settlement buildings.

of about latitude 45° South (the Falklands lie between 51° and 52° South). The flora probably spread south during a period of relatively mild global climate before the start of the last Ice Age a few hundreds of thousands of years ago. Once that was underway the trees were soon wiped out and the Falklands became a barren and windswept polar desert until the Ice Age ended, only about 10 000 years ago.

The modern landscape

The present-day scenery of the Falklands owes a lot to the effects of the last Ice Age. The relatively low-lying islands supported only very small glaciers on the highest peaks, for example Mount Usborne in East Falkland and Mount Robinson and the Hornby Mountains in West Falkland. There, small lakes now occupy the cirques carved out by

Figure 59 This sample of the West Point Island wood was presented to The Natural History Museum, London, in 1909 by the Governor of the Falkland Islands, His Excellency (and later Sir) William Lamond Allardyce. Although the donation is credited to Governor Allardyce, it is more likely that his wife, Constance, was the true benefactor. She took a keen interest in Falklands natural history and established the first local museum collection, for which she acquired several wood samples from Mr Arthur Felton. Felton, the owner of West Point Island at the time, had discovered the 'buried forest' in 1899. © The Natural History Museum, London.

the ice. Elsewhere across the islands, as we have seen, the icy winds carved exposed crags into fantastic shapes and the frost shattered them into the vast piles of rubble from which the stone runs were formed.

The Ice Age also had a dramatic effect on sea level, which fell considerably as so much of the Earth's water became locked into ice. It's because of this phenomenon that most of the Falkland's coastline is today so remarkably indented. It is in fact a drowned river valley system, one that developed when sea level was about 60 m below its present position. As the ice melted and water was released, the sea flooded in to produce the branching and meandering creeks and inlets that characterise the islands (Figure 60). The relationship between the sea and the land is far from straightforward though, and whilst the overall appearance of the coast shows a rise in sea level, there is plenty of evidence for higher sea levels than that of today. In a few places, for example at Pony's Pass Quarry just outside Stanley,

Figure 60 The drowned coast of the Falkland Islands shows that at one time sea level was lower than at present. The oblique aerial view (above) shows Swan Inlet, East Falkland, where the sea has flooded the lower part of a river valley system eroded in orthogonal directions, both of which were controlled by the geological structure. Running east–west (from right to left in the picture) are the low ridges produced by the dip and scarp features of the gently inclined Lafonia Group strata; running approximately north–south are fault zones, components of the set that formed parallel to Falkland Sound. In the ground level view (below), of Bold Cove in West Falkland, the sea has flooded the lower reaches of a river valley eroded parallel to the Coast Ridge in the relatively soft rocks of the Fitzroy Tillite Formation.

there are layers of beach pebbles and boulders a staggering 50 m or more ***above*** present sea level (Figure 61). Along many parts of the coast there are examples of beaches and wave-cut ledges now perched several metres or more above sea level (Figure 62).

After the last Ice Age, the climate started to improve and accumulation of the

Falkland's peat cover began. A widespread peat cover had been initiated by about 10 000 years ago and since then several metres of peat have built up; depths of 3–4 m are fairly common whilst up to 10 m are recorded locally. The thickest peat is way down on the southernmost island of the Falklands archipelago, where a massive 11 m has been measured on Beauchêne Island. Curiously, the lowest peat beds are now below sea level, and in places like Salinas Beach, near Goose Green, the intertidal zone is underlain by peat that also forms a low and readily-eroded cliff at the back of the beach (Figure 63).

Figure 61 Rounded boulders on the edge of Pony's Pass Quarry, near Stanley, East Falkland, now lie about 50 m above sea level but probably accumulated as a boulder beach when sea level was higher than at present. The boulders (arrowed) range up to 50 cm across, though most are smaller, and are now partially obscured by peat and quarry debris.

Peat sea cliffs 4 m high are seen quite close to Stanley, at Hooker's Point (Figure 64), but there they are retreating rapidly in the face of marine erosion. Clearly the peat originally formed from plants that grew above sea level, so the recent relationship of land to sea in the Falklands becomes even more complicated!

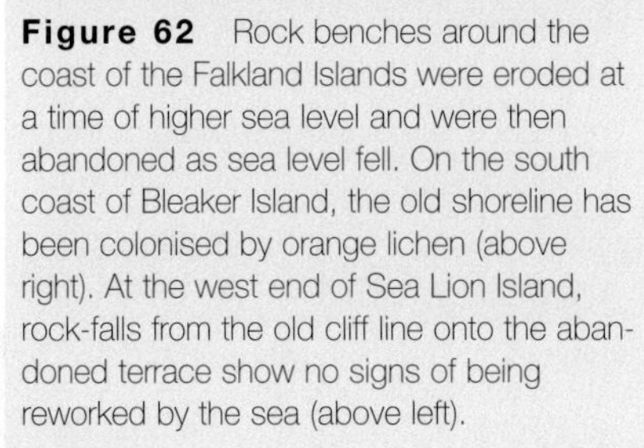

Figure 62 Rock benches around the coast of the Falkland Islands were eroded at a time of higher sea level and were then abandoned as sea level fell. On the south coast of Bleaker Island, the old shoreline has been colonised by orange lichen (above right). At the west end of Sea Lion Island, rock-falls from the old cliff line onto the abandoned terrace show no signs of being reworked by the sea (above left).

Mysteries on the beach

There are still some geological puzzles about the Falklands; one is the origin of the distinctive 'Falkland Pebbles' that are found on some northern beaches. Whilst most of the pebbles on most beaches are derived from the pale grey or brown, local rocks, there are a few places where pebbles with spectacular colours and patterns can be found. Collecting and polishing these is something of a local tradition (Figure 65). These special 'Falkland Pebbles' are agates, silica that accumulated in the cavities left behind when gas escaped from volcanic lavas. Paradoxically, the agates are much harder and resistant to erosion than the lavas that allowed them to form, and so survive long after their host has vanished. There is no lava on the islands today so the pebbles must either be relics of a rock layer that has been completely eroded away, or be washed up on the northern shores of the islands from a source somewhere beneath the sea.

Figure 63 Salinas Beach lies at the head of Brenton Loch and a little to the west of Goose Green, East Falkland. Its intertidal zone is entirely underlain by peat, an extension of the deep onshore accumulations which therefore continue down below present-day mean sea level. At the back of the beach area a low cliff line is eroded in peat. Since the peat was originally formed on dry land a recent rise in sea level looks likely.

And why do some sandy beaches turn pink? Most of the beautiful white beaches of the Falklands are made of sand eroded from the white quartzite rock of the Port Stanley Formation. Although the rock might look to be a completely pure assemblage of quartz grains, it actually contains a very small proportion of red garnet grains. The Fitzroy Tillite also contains a fair amount of garnet. So, the sand eroded from the local rocks also contains a small proportion of tiny red garnets. The garnet grains are much denser and heavier than the sand grains and so are often left behind when wind or waves move the sand. As the garnet proportion slowly builds up in the sand left behind, so the beach turns pink (Figure 66).

Figure 64 At Hooker's Point, not far from Stanley, East Falkland, peat forms a coastal cliff 4–5 m high that is being rapidly eroded back by the sea.

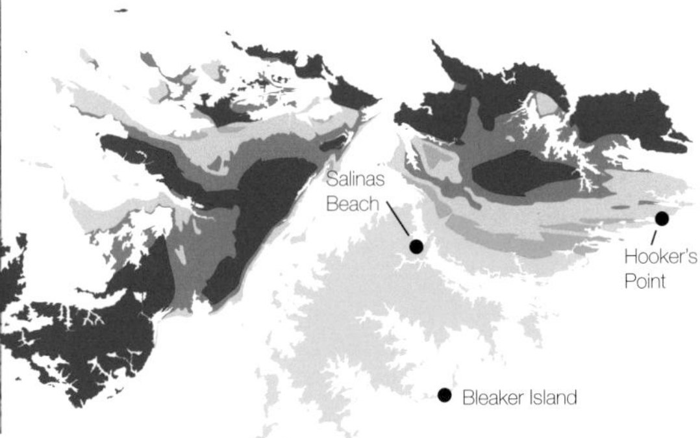

Some of the white, sandy beaches are very different though. In a few places the sand grains are not made from quartz but from the broken-up remains of shells and lime-rich algal encrustations. The latter are particular interesting — and useful. They are formed by varieties of red algae that live offshore in the clear, shallow water, extract calcium carbonate (lime) from it and then build up concentric limey layers in which to live. Sometimes the layers form crusts on sea-floor rocks but commonly the limey layers build up into irregular balls that are free to roll around with the current, and often get washed onto the shore (Figure 67) where the algae dies and the balls break up. The resulting fine-grained, lime-rich sand is known in the Falklands as *calcified seaweed* (elsewhere in the World it is often called *maerl*) and is locally extracted from beaches in a carefully controlled manner (Figure 68) to provide a useful fertiliser for the acidic Falklands' soils. There is no limestone in the Falklands' rock succession, and so no alternative, indigenous source of lime, a fundamental agricultural commodity.

Rock around Stanley

All of the rocky crags that you can see around Stanley are composed of the hard, white quartzite that makes up the Port Stanley Formation; the same rock type that gives rise to the stone runs. Blocks of quartzite have been used in various buildings around the town, most prominently in Christ Church Cathedral (Figure 69) but most poignantly in the 1982 Liberation

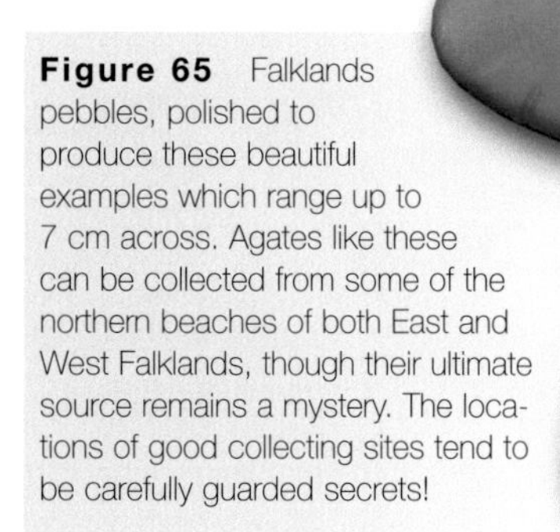

Figure 65 Falklands pebbles, polished to produce these beautiful examples which range up to 7 cm across. Agates like these can be collected from some of the northern beaches of both East and West Falklands, though their ultimate source remains a mystery. The locations of good collecting sites tend to be carefully guarded secrets!

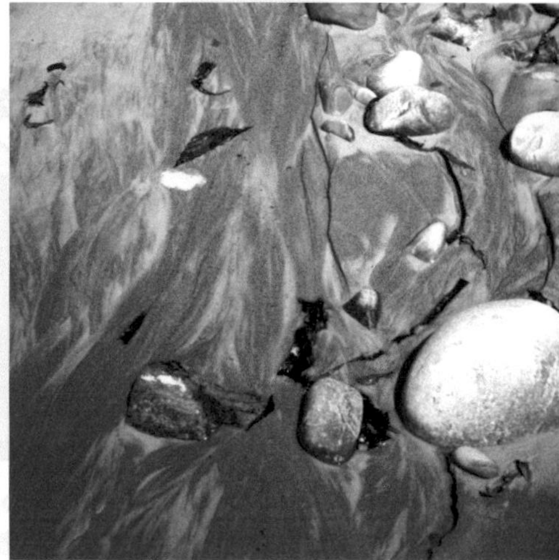

Figure 66 Pink sand on beaches around Cape Pembroke, East Falkland. The colour is produced by a concentration of relatively dense grains of red garnet that are left behind as the lighter sand grains, mostly made of quartz, are winnowed away by wind and waves.

Monument (Figure 70), where the quartzite blocks forming the curved, rear wall were collected from the battlefield sites west of Stanley, along the mountain ridge formed by the Port Stanley Formation. There is actually some uncertainty over the origin of the cathedral building stone, with a local tradition that it was imported from Britain. What is known is that much of the material for the cathedral, built between 1890 and 1892, was recycled from the earlier Exchange Building that

Figure 67 Balls of calcified seaweed washed ashore at Brown Harbour, West Falkland. These are *rhodoliths* produced as marine red algae extracted calcium carbonate from the seawater and deposited it in concentric layers.

Figure 68 Extraction of calcified seaweed in progress at Ruggles Bay, East Falkland. It is used in agriculture and horticulture to improve soil and pasture quality.

was erected on the same site in 1852 but demolished after suffering damage in a devastating peat slip in 1886. The building stone certainly looks a lot like Stanley quartzite so make a closer inspection and see what you think.

An unequivocal site is the ornamental garden in the King Edward VII Hospital, created in 2002 by the BBC's 'Groundforce' television gardening team. For the paved area (Figure 71) they used flagstones quarried from the Fox Bay Formation near Fox Bay itself on West Falkland (Figure 72) and ornamental pebbles and boulders of local Stanley quartzite. Another attractive combination of quartzite blocks and flagstones can be seen at the primary school in John Street, whilst a laminated variety of Stanley quartzite has been expertly used for the wall outside the Tabernacle in Barrack Street. Fox Bay flagstones have been used as an ornamental facing in several Stanley buildings, for example the Malvina House Hotel, but the similar-looking paving slabs around the 1982 memorial are actually imported 'York Stone', a Carboniferous sandstone from

Figure 69 Christ Church Cathedral, Stanley, East Falkland. Is it constructed from blocks of Port Stanley Formation quartzite?

the north of England. The granite blocks for both the 1982 memorial and that commemorating the 1914 Battle of the Falklands also came from England; from granite quarries in Devon and Cornwall respectively.

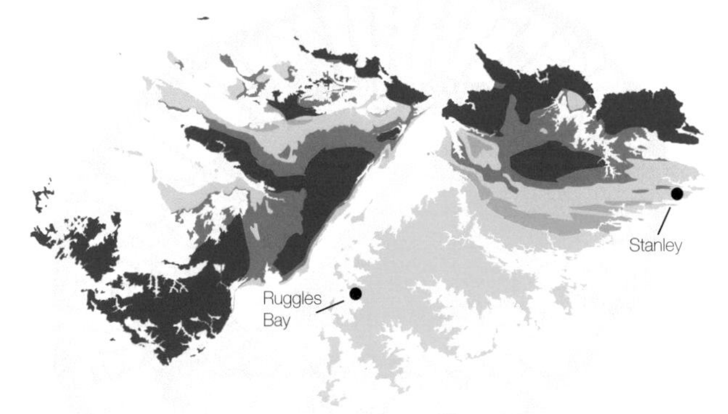

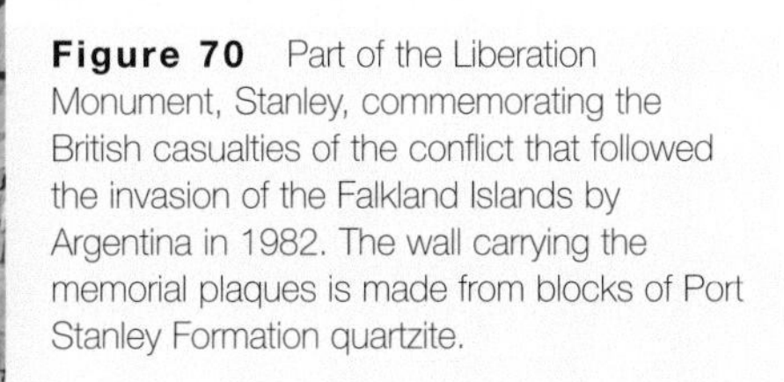

Figure 70 Part of the Liberation Monument, Stanley, commemorating the British casualties of the conflict that followed the invasion of the Falkland Islands by Argentina in 1982. The wall carrying the memorial plaques is made from blocks of Port Stanley Formation quartzite.

The future

The rocks of the Falkland Islands are a fundamental influence on the territory's

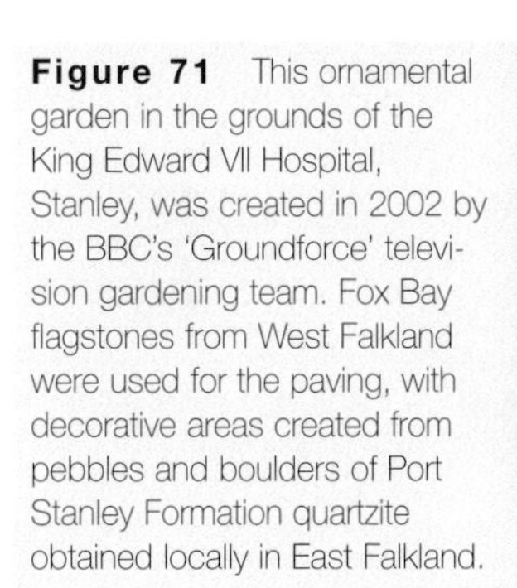

Figure 71 This ornamental garden in the grounds of the King Edward VII Hospital, Stanley, was created in 2002 by the BBC's 'Groundforce' television gardening team. Fox Bay flagstones from West Falkland were used for the paving, with decorative areas created from pebbles and boulders of Port Stanley Formation quartzite obtained locally in East Falkland.

unique, memorable landscape; the fossils form an important part of a rich cultural heritage. Together they tell a fascinating and dramatic story of drifting continents and the ancient life that they supported. But now, at the beginning of the 21st century, there is optimism that the rocks may soon make a more direct contribution to the economic well-being of the islanders. The offshore sedimentary basins, created as the Falklands drifted westwards with the spreading Atlantic Ocean, are being explored for their oil potential (Figure 73). Meanwhile, onshore, gold grains in stream gravels (Figure 74) are being traced back to their source in the hope that significant accumulations of the metal will be discovered. It would not be the first time that gold has

Figure 72 Fox Bay Formation flagstones at source near Fox Bay, West Falkland. The distant hill is Mount Sulivan.

Fox Bay

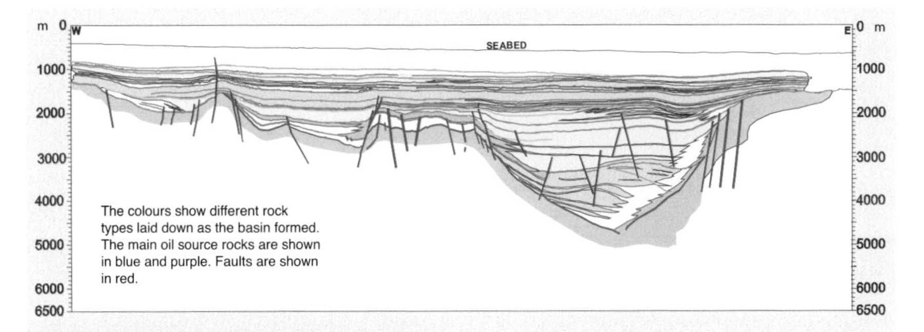

Figure 73 A composite geological section across the North Falklands Basin, developed from seismic data and drilling results. The 'basin' is a geological graben structure between 30 and 50 km across but extending northwards for at least 230 km from a southern margin only 36 km north of the Falklands' north coast, as shown in Figure 75.

contributed to the Falklands' economy. Back in the 1880s Stanley was an important staging post for ships carrying would-be miners around Cape Horn to the California gold rush, with the hulk of the *Vicar of Bray* at Goose Green in Darwin Harbour, a monument to those dangerous days.

Offshore oil exploration maintains the maritime tradition but brings to bear the panoply of modern technology. The offshore basins (Figure 75) formed as the Earth's crust stretched and subsided during the growth of the Atlantic Ocean. As they formed, so they were filled by sediment containing abundant organic material, but these potential fossils weren't preserved; instead they generated liquid hydrocarbons — oil. The innermost secrets of the sediment-filled basins can be probed by seismic waves, artificially generated by equipment carried on board ships, which penetrate through

Figure 74 Gold grains extracted from the sandy bed of a Falkland Islands stream. Picture supplied by Derek Reeves, Falkland Minerals Limited.

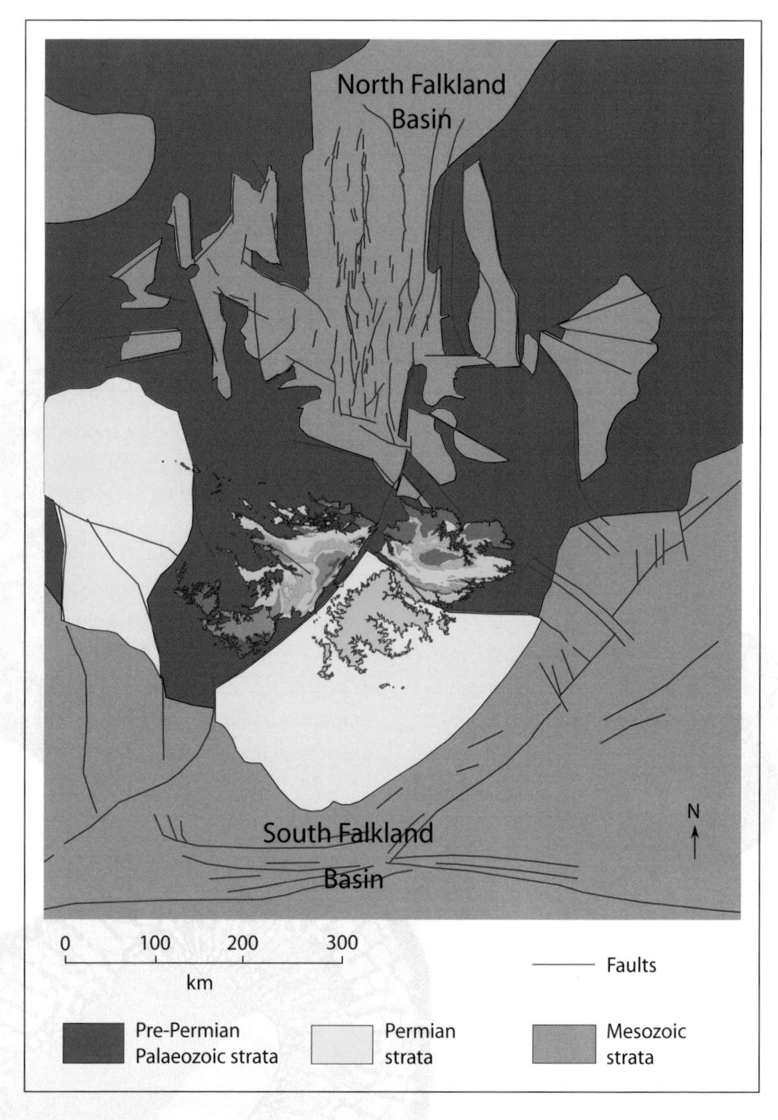

Figure 75 An outline of the geology of the offshore area surrounding the Falkland Islands.

the layers of sediment with variable degrees of reflection or refraction at different boundaries. As the seismic waves bounce back to the surface they can be detected and measured. From the results, profiles across the basins are built up (Figure 73) and the most likely sites for oil accumulation are assessed and then drilled. Drilling into the seabed beneath the waters of the South Atlantic is no mean feat, but the first six exploratory wells were successfully sunk in 1998, the deepest penetrating 4000 m of sediment beneath 460 m of water! Nothing is certain, but the search continues in the hope that the Falkland Islands' distant past will be the key to their prosperous future.

BIBLIOGRAPHY

The following scientific papers are of historical interest and were of particular importance in shaping our understanding of Falkland Islands geology.

ADIE, R J. 1952. The position of the Falkland Islands in a reconstruction of Gondwanaland. *Geological Magazine*, Vol.89, 401–410.

ANDERSSON, J G. 1907. Contributions to the geology of the Falkland Islands. *Wissenschaftliche Ergebnisse der Schwedischen Sudpolar-expedition 1901–1903*, Vol.3 (Lief. 2), 38 pp.

BAKER, H A. 1924. *Final Report on Geological Investigations in the Falkland Islands, 1920–1922*. Stanley, Government Printer.

DARWIN, C R. 1846. On the geology of the Falkland Islands. *Quarterly Journal of the Geological Society of London*, Vol.2, 267–274.

FRAKES, L A, and CROWELL, J C. 1967. Facies and paleogeography of Late Paleozoic Diamictite, Falkland Islands. *Geological Society of America Bulletin*, Vol.78, 37–58.

GREENWAY, M E. 1972. The geology of the Falkland Islands. *British Antarctic Survey, Scientific Report*, No.76.

HALLE, T G. 1912. On the geological structure and history of the Falkland Islands. *Bulletin of the Geological Institution of the University of Uppsala*, Vol.11, 115–229.

The following scientific papers provide an introduction to the modern literature and have been particularly useful in the preparation of this book.

ALDISS, D T, and EDWARDS, E J. 1999. The Geology of the Falkland Islands. *British Geological Survey Technical Report*, WC/99/10.

CLARK, R, EDWARDS, E, LUXTON, S, SHIPP, T, and WILSON, P. 1995. Geology in the Falkland Islands. *Geology Today*, Vol.11, 217–223.

CURTIS, M L, and HYAM, D M. 1998. Late Palaeozoic to Mesozoic structural evolution of the Falkland Islands: a displaced segment of the Cape Fold Belt. *Journal of the Geological Society of London*, Vol.155, 115–129.

HUNTER, M A, and LOMAS, S A. 2003. Reconstructing the Siluro-Devonian coastline of Gondwana: insights from the sedimentology of the Port Stephens Formation, Falkland Islands. *Journal of the Geological Society of London*, Vol.160, 459–476.

JACOBS, J, THOMAS, R J, ARMSTRONG, R A, and HENJES-KUNST, F. 1999. Age and thermal evolution of the Mesoproterozoic Cape Meredith Complex, West Falkland. *Journal of the Geological Society of London*, Vol.156, 917–928.

MARSHALL, J E A. 1994. The Falkland Islands: a key element in Gondwana palaeogeography. *Tectonics*, Vol.13, 499–514.

POWELL, C MCA, and LI, Z X. 1994. Reconstruction of the Panthalassan margin of Gondwanaland. 5–9 in *Permian – Triassic Pangean basins and foldbelts along the Panthalassan margin of Gondwanaland*. VEEVERS, J J, and POWELL C MCA. (editors). Geological Society of America Memoir, Vol.184.

RICHARDS, P C, GATLIFF, R W, QUINN, M F, WILLIAMSON, J P, and FANNIN, N G T. 1996. The geological evolution of the Falkland Islands continental shelf. 105–128 in *Weddell Sea Tectonics and Gondwana Break-up*. STOREY, B C, KING, E C, and LIVERMORE, R A. (editors). Geological Society of London, Special Publication No. 108.

STONE, P, and RUSHTON, A W A. 2003. Some new fossil records and *notabilia* from the Falkland Islands. *Falkland Island Journal*, Vol.8 (2), 1–10.

STOREY, B C, CURTIS, M L, FERRIS, J K, HUNTER, M A, and LIVERMORE, R A. 1999. Reconstruction and break-out model for the Falkland Islands within Gondwana. *Journal of African Earth Sciences*, Vol.29, 153–163.

TREWIN, N H, MACDONALD, D I M, and THOMAS, C G C. 2002. Stratigraphy and sedimentology of the Permian of the Falkland Islands: lithostratigraphic and palaeoenvironmental links with South Africa. *Journal of the Geological Society of London*, Vol.159, 5–19.